History's Dumbest
INVENTIONS

METRO BOOKS
New York

An Imprint of Sterling Publishing Co., Inc.
1166 Avenue of the Americas
New York, NY 10036

ISBN 978-1-4351-7109-1

For information about custom editions, special sales, and premium and corporate
purchases, please contact Sterling Special Sales at 800-805-5489
or specialsales@sterlingpublishing.com

Manufactured in Singapore

2 4 6 8 10 9 7 5 3 1

sterlingpublishing.com

Additional text by Melissa Umbarger, Guy Campbell, and Charles Phillips
Design and illustrations by Steve Wildish

History's Dumbest
INVENTIONS

Historical Tales of Goofy Gadgets,
Ill-advised Innovations, and Devious Devices

ZOË WILDSMITH & DEVON LARA LUCAS

METRO BOOKS
New York

CONTENTS

Cyclomer amphibious bike (1932). It didn't work on land. Or water.

INTRODUCTION

Necessity is the mother of invention (tell that to the inventor of the strapless cup bra) but that doesn't mean that even the most brilliant of inventors—yes, we're thinking of you, Leonardo—can't come up with downright bonkers ideas at times.

We all have it in us to be dumb. And sometimes inventors get so caught up in the sheer brilliance of their idea, they, well… don't pay attention to detail: Illuminated tires, anyone? Not to mention those inventors for whom the lure of fame and fortune is too strong, so a brilliant idea is badly executed. Or they just lie and pretend their invention does something when it doesn't—the earthquake machine was never going to catch on anyway.

Then there are the good inventions that would have benefitted from a teensy bit of foresight, to see the potential impact that one seemingly innocent invention could have (we're looking at you and your CFCs, Thomas Midgely Jr.!).

As you will see, stupidity comes in many forms, but as Edison himself said: "Many of life's failures are people who did not realize how close they were to success when they gave up."

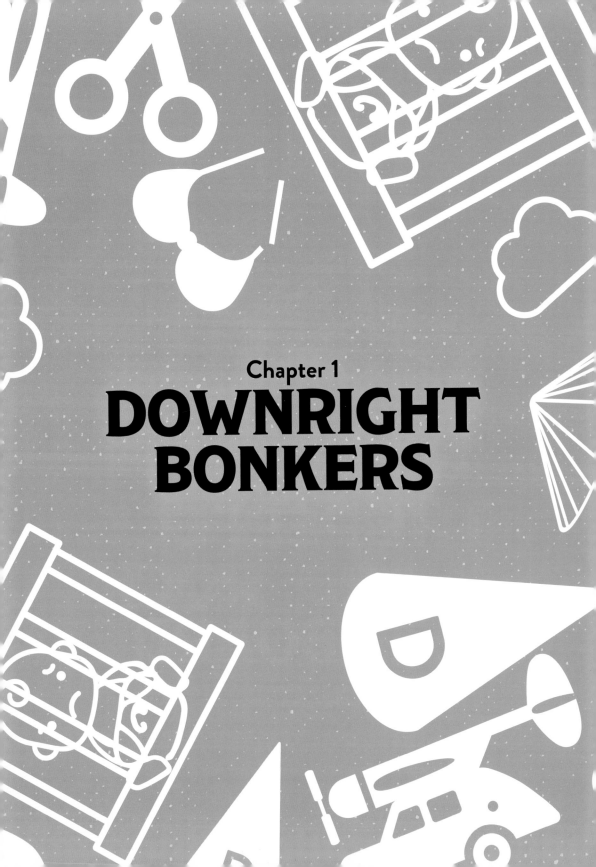

Chapter 1

DOWNRIGHT BONKERS

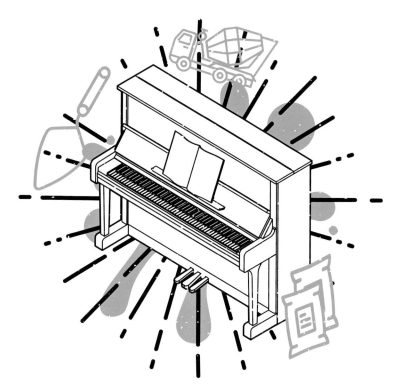

#1 THE CONCRETE PIANO

THE PERFECT "HARD" ROCK KEYBOARD

c.1899 | New Jersey

Thomas Edison's inventiveness took some strange directions—
not least in designing this super-heavyweight musical
instrument: the concrete piano.

#1 The Concrete Piano

You wouldn't want to drop the lid of this piano onto your fingers. Thomas Edison was on a drive to promote his own-brand cement and his idea of affordable concrete houses when he came up with the idea of the concrete piano. A Steinway it wasn't!

Edison tops many lists as one of the most prolific inventors in history. He invented yada, yada, yada, and don't forget the important thing, plus all that other stuff. Perhaps you've heard of his Talking Doll (see p. 88)? Before he died, he was quoted as saying: "If I had not had so much ambition and had not tried to do so many things, I probably would have been happier but less useful." Not sure that "useful" was always the correct word, considering his many failures, but he certainly was busy!

One industry in which he adventured was the world of cement. In 1897, he started tinkering around with an ore-crushing technology that left over an exceptionally fine sand. He sold it to merchants making portland cement (the most common type) and they were ecstatic. Why stop there? He decided that he would join the community of cement-makers and started his own business. He recruited investors and founded the Edison Portland Cement Company around 1899. The mill was located near Ogdensburg, New Jersey, on the Delaware River. In it, he built the largest rotating kilns in the world at that time—each one was 150 feet (45 m) long. Go big or go home! Unsatisfied with stopping at his already perfect cement, he discovered that by adding air to the compound, it created a sort of "foam" that was much lighter than traditional cement. It was such a novelty that people were clamoring to purchase it and make it— and this led to an excess in the industry.

Raise the Roof

Never one to sit idly by, Edison birthed the idea of using the material to make entire houses. He wished for dwellings with multiple floors and many bedrooms. The houses would be immune to bugs, would be fireproof, and a cinch to clean. Colors that would appeal to the consumer could be mixed into the cement, saving them the hassle of painting the walls. Using only one mold that could be recycled repeatedly, an entire floor of the house could be created in a matter of hours with all of the details included.

Edison with a model of a concrete house. On a VERY strong table.

"If I had not had so much ambition and had not tried to do so many things, I probably would have been happier but less useful."

—Thomas Edison

#1 The Concrete Piano

The cherry on top would be the cost of manufacturing the homes. At $1,200, each one would be cheap and affordable. Anyone could own a house. It was the American Dream at its finest.

He spent seven long years trying to make these homes a reality and convince others of their genius. But no one was biting. Not a single house was actually poured into existence. During the time, he branched out even further and decided that he wanted to create anything in the house that could be made out of the material: Ornate decorations molded right into the walls. Comfy couches! Plush beds! Fridges! Pianos! Heck, even a tombstone for the house owner for their passing. The sky was the limit. The idea of a concrete piano excited him the most. As the inventor of the phonograph, he already had a keen interest in bringing music to the general public. He passionately exclaimed, "Music is so helpful to the human mind that it is naturally a source of satisfaction to me that I have helped in some way to make the very finest music available to millions." Along with his houses being cheaply made, the piano would also be easy to produce and affordable to anyone who wanted to own one. Everyone could share music.

The piano would be concrete on the outside, with ornate details molded in. On a traditional piano these types of markings were hand-carved, which brought the piano's cost up even higher. A wooden soundboard would rest inside. The piano could be painted to look similar in color to a traditional wood piano. It wouldn't be the perfect housing for the instrument but would certainly be functional and affordable. One company in 1931 developed a few, but the idea did not catch on. Funny, that. Concrete is not known for its sound resonance properties, which are pretty key to a good piano.

Concrete Proof

All in all, Edison's entire endeavor of creating the perfect home and all its accessories out of concrete was a disaster. No one wanted to buy or produce any of it. The company went bankrupt multiple times and ended up in a mountain of debt. The concrete house dream had crumbled with the concrete pianos. Don't worry, though. He had plenty more ideas and moved right on to the next one.

#2 THE BABY CAGE

HANGING BABY OUT TO... PLAY?

c.1900 | New York City, New York

You live in a city, in a tall building with no yard or balcony. How are you going to ensure your baby gets sufficient fresh, healthy, city air? Simple! Pop your darling in a baby cage, securely fastened (you hope) to the window of your building—however many stories up you are!

#2 The Baby Cage

At the end of the nineteenth century, sunlight and fresh air were believed to purify the blood and to be as important as food for good health, for both adults and children. Tuberculosis patients in hospitals were prescribed two hours of outside air per day as part of their treatment. In 1894, Dr. Luther Emmett Holt emphasized the benefits of babies getting plenty of air and sunlight in his book *The Care and Feeding of Children*, which led to parents leaving their young children in strollers in their backyards in all weathers—urbanites even started putting them to sleep in boxes on roofs and balconies in order to develop their "fresh air training."

By the turn of the century it was not unusual to see babies rather than flowerpots gracing precipitously high balconies and roof gardens, so the baby cage's appearance around that time makes perfect sense. Okay, there were potential safety hazards, but let's gloss over those for now and think of all that healthful fresh air!

As city-dwelling increased both in the United States and England, the baby cage became a viable solution for giving babies their fresh-air fix in a bid to stave off all-too-common lung diseases. It is not known who can be thanked for conceptualizing the first baby cage, which pretty much is what it sounds like—a wire cage open to the elements, hung from a window. An early adopter of the practice was Eleanor Roosevelt in 1906. She improvised on her townhouse and aired out her first child in a chicken cage, causing neighbors to be so horrified by her baby's crying they threatened to call the child-protection authorities. Around the same time, though, writer Louis Fischer was penning a baby care book that included a "Boggins' Window Crib." It was essentially an outdoor sleeping area to attach to city windows, with screens to keep out bugs and, most importantly, to stop the baby from rolling out.

In 1923, Emma Read from Spokane, WA, got a patent for a portable baby cage. Not content with hanging your baby out of your homestead high-rise? Take your cage on your travels and suspend your unsuspecting infant out of any city window you choose.

Read's design was the penthouse of baby cages—a step up from the simple wire box. She made sure there was a roof to keep out rain and snow (considerate) and ample room for toys, so the baby or young child could play. There was also space for bedding should the infant need to nap (How long exactly were they planning to keep baby in there? Why stop at toys and bedding, where's the potty and dining area?) Read's detachable prototypes were even equipped with a pulley system of roll-down drapes to shelter the child from strong winds that might wake them but which would still allow enough air to circulate—let's not forget our common goal here, folks. Gotta get that fresh, thick, city air.

Decades of Caged Children

After their use through the 1920s, baby cages—still made from wire fabric or bars— were hung from several tall buildings in London in the 1930s, as their popularity grew. Despite the obvious risks of suspending a child from a building, unsupervised, using a few brackets and spindly wires, some councils even endorsed their use in keeping children healthful and they were distributed by parenting group the Chelsea Baby Club to its members. Architects soon got in on the act and designed homes with built-in baby balconies. They were deemed so important by some parents that Blitz-damaged homes had their baby cages reinstalled after World War II.

Safety issues aside, let's not rule out another strong factor in the baby cage's favor: minimizing the diaper smells! No more eau de poop in the apartment, let Mother Nature take it away with the wind. All things considered, it's a wonder this idea died out in the latter half of the twentieth century.

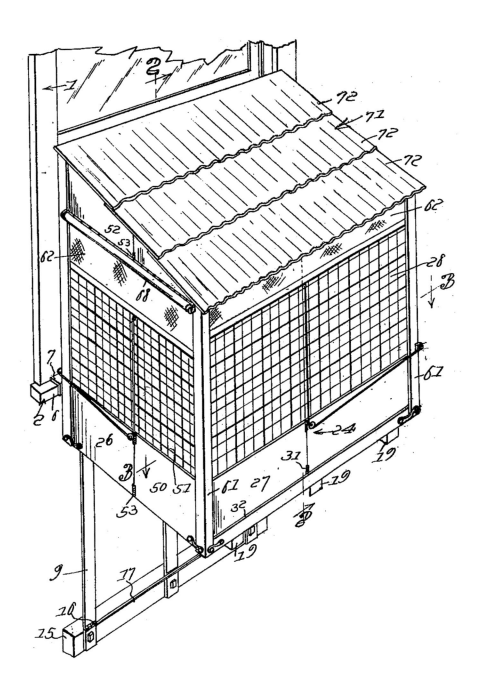

Read's patent plans for a portable rabbit hutch. Wait. Baby cage.

#3 THE READING MACHINE
A LITTLE (VERY) LIGHT READING

1922 | Washington, D.C.

A device that makes for a cheap and portable book collection sounds like a winner. Not if it turns out to be a headache to use...

#3 The Reading Machine

Rear Admiral Bradley A. Fiske was a naval officer known for inventing a range of technical devices for the military. In addition to his impressive career as an officer who climbed the ranks, Fiske was also a prolific writer who wanted the general public to understand the navy. He was heralded for inventing the electric range finder, a device that does pretty much what its name implies.

After he retired from the military, he had time on his hands, and he used it to continue tinkering. He was certainly not showing signs of slowing down. In 1921, he published *Invention: The Master-Key to Progress*. In the prologue he writes: "The mind of man cannot even conceive what wonders of beneficence inventors may accomplish: for the resources of invention are infinite." He was clearly a man of great intelligence. But he invented one item where you might argue his resources of invention were a bit more finite.

In the early 1920s, he wanted books to be portable in a way that e-readers are for us lucky readers today. Minus the electronic aspect, of course. Books were hefty and expensive and each one only contained a single story. He wanted a way to take multiple volumes wherever he went without the hassle of filling up a book bag and hauling it around. He thought books should be cheaper, in general, and felt that all people should be able to afford to read. With all of his experience in naval tech, he had plenty of gadgets at his disposal. A magnifying glass, in particular, was employed for the creation of the Fiske Reading Machine.

Mr. Inventive's idea was to reduce the size of an entire book to about one-hundredth of its original extent onto thick, tiny cards that were 2 inches by 6 inches (5 cm by 15 cm): 10,000 words could be printed on each side of the card. The cards were fed into a small, handheld device that allowed the reader to scroll through the words, reading through a magnifying glass. There was a blinder built in so that the reader could focus properly on the words without getting distracted. And it only weighed a little more than 5 oz (around 150 g). He even claimed that people could read more words per minute with the device than if they were reading a book.

Ready, Set, Read!

To prove that his invention was viable, he started out with Mark Twain's 1869 book *The Innocents Abroad*, a book with around 93,000 words. He shrank the text onto thirteen of the tiny cards and then set out to show off the prototype. The idea started gaining momentum. *Scientific American* wrote an article in support of the apparatus, listing its advantages. The "books" would be cheaper to make, because they used less paper materials and smaller machines to produce them. They would use "better quality paper" that was more durable. And people could stop using glasses to read. Plus, there would be so much more room in the house to fill with other collections! You're welcome, hoarders.

The invention was covered by other prestigious publications and the concept received lots of support. Fiske filed for several patents and felt he'd created something that would change the world of publishing. He was ready to make a mint on the product. To be perfectly frank, in some ways it was pretty genius. But the timing wasn't right.

Not So Fast, Speed Reader

Unfortunately, Fiske was up against formidable competition. A great example was the mass-market publishing industry itself. They were busy figuring out ways to make their books cheaper around the same time. They certainly didn't want to lose profits on the works they'd been hard at producing. And Kodak was working on microfiche technology. Their success came in 1935 when they officially started publishing *The New York Times* on microfilm. You remember scrolling through newspapers on a computer in the library, whizzing right past whatever you were trying to locate, and then repeating the process indefinitely, yes?

But mostly, books were there to stay. The public was just fine with hoisting them around. How could you show off your superior literary taste if passersby couldn't read the title of the F. Scott Fitzgerald book you were carrying? With so much competition, the enthusiasm for the Fiske Reading Machine died down and (we're pretty sure) the device was buried under a giant stack of books.

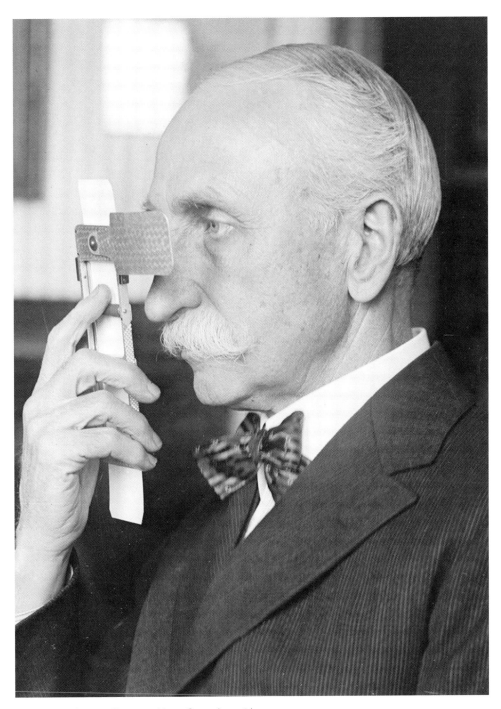

Fiske using his reading machine. Or so he said.

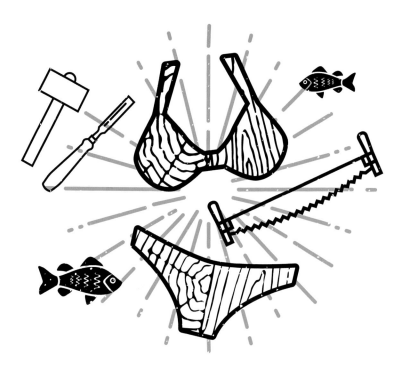

#4 THE WOODEN BATHING SUIT

WHY WOODEN YOU WANT ONE?

1929 | Grays Harbor County, Washington

In the late 1920s, consumers could go out and buy bathing suits made from... wood. Some ideas are straightforwardly dumb, others are seriously weird. This one is off the charts.

#4 The Wooden Bathing Suit

In Grays Harbor County, Washington, no tree is safe. It's an area of the country that has long been associated with the wood industry. In the beginning of the 1900s, it earned its title as one of the largest producers and exporters on the planet. In fact, one historian was quoted as saying, "Grays Harbor would be the only lumber port in the world able to talk in billions while others were talking millions in the lumber game." That is a LOT of wood talk. Today a sign boasting "Lumber Capital of the World" proudly welcomes guests to Aberdeen, WA, located in the heart of Grays Harbor.

The types of items that left the area in the early 1900s included enormous logs, massive beams, planks of all sizes and shapes, and shingles. Tens of thousands of workers were employed in the area to process and ship the wood worldwide. One of the locally grown tree species was spruce. This particular type of wood was great for making thin strips of veneer. It was cheap to produce and showed off a nice wood grain pattern. Products that are meant to look nice but cost less are still often accented with spruce.

One crafty genius came up with the idea of expanding the use of this flexible wood into apparel in the late 1920s. Legend has it that after a citizen finished building his family's house, there was some spruce veneer left over. His daughter noticed it and decided to make a bathing suit out of the materials. The identity of this smarty pants remains a mystery, but she certainly created a spectacle! Around this time, people wanted ways to feel more comfortable in open water, as it posed dangers to weaker swimmers. Wood was known to float, and people liked floating in water. Well, really, they liked not drowning in it. These suits basically had a built-in life jacket! It should be noted that at the time, Germans were busy wrapping themselves in bicycle tires as flotation devices. Not sure who wins that competition.

Shingle and Ready to Mingle
Though they might seem kind of wacko, the suits were actually pretty functional. They were cheap to source, easy to put together, and they certainly were unique. The basic bathing suit used a thin strip of the spruce veneer long enough to cover

the torso and thighs of the wearer and it wrapped around the body in one piece. It was secured at the waist with a belt, often shown in different styles indicating that a bit of individuality was encouraged. Some had a strip of fabric (wood?) that ran from the top of the suit over the shoulder and attached at the back for extra security. A pair of shorts (or bloomers) were seen peeking out from underneath. These were also made with the wood. Models were shown sitting, standing, and frolicking in the water looking pretty content. More on these ladies in a bit.

In the summer of 1929, Grays Harbor wanted to step up the visibility of all they'd accomplished in the lumber industry. Today we can celebrate exciting holidays like "National Fruitcake Toss" in early January and "Talk Like A Pirate Day" in September, but at that time, basic traditional holidays were the ones recognized. The county came up with a celebration called Wood Week (which was just asking for jokes to be made). Perhaps they were observing National Beer Day when they brainstormed?

Move Over, Spice Girls
Along with the weeklong fest, an advertising campaign was created to sell the newly devised swimsuits. This led to the introduction of the Spruce Girls. These lovely ladies were photographed modeling the wooden suits in all sorts of situations and the photographs were the main attraction left over after the celebration ended. The best one is of three of them holding a GIANT umbrella, casually showing off the fashion.

Although the suits never made it internationally, *Popular Science* covered the trend, saying they were "practical as costumes and also are sufficiently buoyant to encourage a timid swimmer to take a plunge." Even better, "so far, none of them has warped or cracked."

The "Spruce Girls" show off their wooden bathing suits during "Wood Week,"
Washington, ca. 1929.

#5 THE CUP BRA
FRILLS AND SPILLS

1948 | Detroit, Michigan

Who needs bras, and straps, when you can have adhesive breast covers called "Posĕs"? In fact, these "cup-shaped pockets" may be all you need to wear on top.

#5 The Cup Bra

The most uncomfortable parts of a bra are the straps and buckles. Plus, they create ugly tan marks on the beach and are not attractive if they slide into view underneath a skimpy top or strapless dress. So here's an idea, thought Detroit-based, 1940s' inventor Charles L. Langs, responding to a need he observed in his wife, Mary: Why not eliminate the breath-restricting, rib-cage-compressing elastic that fastens around the middle, and lose those pesky straps that dig in and weigh a woman's neck and shoulders down?

Remove the straps and you're left with... the cups! And, er, no support. But let's not get bogged down in details, shall we?

A Sticky Problem

Madonna has nothing on this inventor. In the late 1940s, Lang developed and marketed pointy, frilly cups that could be stuck onto women's bosoms like little party hats. They were disposable cups to be worn on the beach to avoid suntan strap marks, with evening-wear (for example, with a backless ball gown), or even just when relaxing at home. Now that the war was over and food was in better supply, instead of loosening her bra to make more room, Langs' wife could overindulge at mealtimes, strap-free, while wearing a frou-frou cone on each breast... Perhaps a different design on each side, because Lang produced stick-on, pointy cups in an array of colors and fabric designs. He stopped short of adding tassels.

Langs worked in the motor industry by trade, chrome-plating automotive grilles. He called on another Charles for help in devising a strong, safe surgical-tape-like adhesive that could easily be removed from the skin. Industrial chemist Charles W. Walton worked by day at what is now 3M, the company that invented Micropore surgical tape, and would later become senior vice president of R&D there. Before Micropore was developed, Walton worked with Langs to create his cup-bra glue. In 1948 Langs applied for a patent for the "Breast Cover... attached directly to the body, e.g. by means of adhesive."

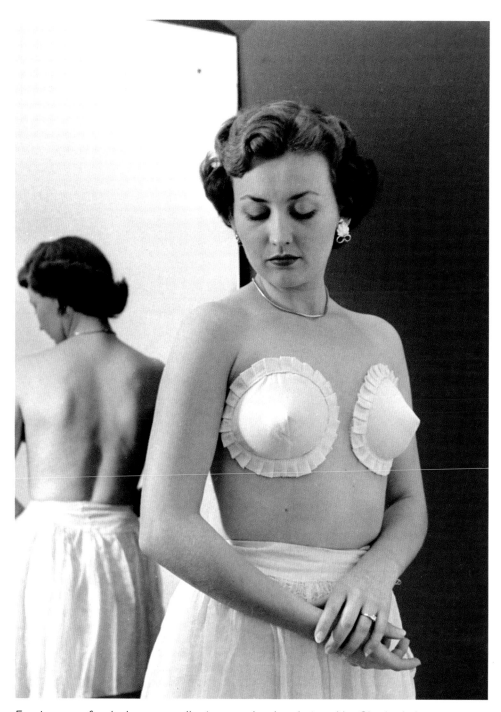

Evening gown for the brave: an adhesive, strapless bra designed by Charles L. Langs.

Langs gave his invention a name: the Posěs, pronounced "posies." He was aiming for sturdy and discreet—apart from the frills (flanges) around the edges, which looked not unlike the necks of certain lizards when threatened. They were robust enough to stay on during a game of tennis, no less, if the promotional pictures of women wearing nothing but a tennis skirt and two tiny teepees were anything to go by. The "cup-shaped pockets" came with a built-in layer of the special adhesive that held them fast to the chest, even while diving and swimming (with hope, and a prayer), but they could be painlessly peeled off after use. They were made large enough so that the adhesive-lined flanges didn't make contact with the "tender" breast area and cause bruising.

Sold Out

Credit where credit is due, though. Astonishingly, the idea took off. Sun-seeking women couldn't get enough of the Posěs. Literally. They sold out and Langs couldn't keep up with demand, leaving customers out of pocket and out of patience. Unfortunately, some of those who did manage to get their hands on a pair (and a pair on their bosoms), turned out to be allergic to the revolutionary adhesive. And the cup-bra fad died out just around the time Langs was finally granted his patent in 1951. It turned out an epic fail: What a boob, Charles.

Brassieres through the Ages

Ancient Greeks and Romans wore bra-like strips of cloth or bands to support their breasts. Corsets kept women's busts uncomfortably in check for several hundred years until Mary Phelps Jacob joined two handkerchiefs with a ribbon and patented one of the first approximations of a modern brassiere in 1914. Conical "bullet" bras became popular in the 1940s and padding and underwiring were added to the undergarments. In 1963 the first push-up Wonderbra was launched, but women had to wait until 1977 for Lisa Lindahl and others to invent a sports bra (never mind, meantime Langs' cup bras would have to do).

#6 THE FLYING CAR
ON A WING AND A PRAYER

1973 | Los Angeles, California

A futuristic "roadable aircraft" for commuters? When its wing began to come off during a test flight, the inventors were undeterred, but then the wing actually fell off during its second…

#6 The Flying Car

In the early 1970s, Los Angeles aeronautical engineers Henry Smolinski and Harold "Hal" Blake came up with the idea of a flying car with detachable wings. The idea behind the hybrid vehicle was to enable a door-to-door commute. The hybrid auto-plane was not a new concept—in fact, inventor Robert Edison Fulton Jr. constructed the wonderfully named Fulton Airphibian in 1946, which was a technical triumph but a financial flop that was grounded by its expense. Others attempted to build flying cars, but none got anywhere near success.

Enter the AVE Mizar: The griffin of vehicles. Prototypes were a hybrid of a Ford Pinto with a Cessna Skymaster's wings stuck on the back, like the offspring of an airplane–automobile love-in. This composite craft also had the benefit of two engines (one from the plane, one from the car), giving the option of more power in order to reduce the takeoff run-up if needed. It must be said the Pinto seemed a strange choice to some—as its safety reputation bombed after frequent reports of it bursting into flames when rear-ended.

Advanced... if Sexist

AVE stands for Advanced Vehicle Engineers, a company founded in 1968 by Smolinski and Blake along with Lois A. MacDonald, an "attractive blonde pilot" (as local Van Nuys newspaper *The Valley News* described her at the time, in typical 1970s style). The vehicle had detachable wings that attached to the Pinto via runners in two minutes, ready for takeoff. Four strong, self-locking pins were used to keep the wings in place. On landing, the journey could be completed by road, once the wings had been quickly unbolted. More of that delightful 1970s attitude to equality came from inventor Smolinski, who said while promoting the vehicle that it was so easy to assemble that "a woman can easily put the two systems together—or separate them—without help."

The car's instrument panel incorporated flight-control instruments. Turning the steering wheel moved the ailerons during flight. Pushing or pulling the steering wheel controlled the elevators, which were movable tail parts for changing the angle of the aircraft. The contraption could fly at 130 mph (210 kmph) at a maximum altitude of 12,000 feet (3,700 m) and with a range of around 1,000 miles (1,600 km). Its stopping distance on landing was 530 feet (around 160 m), which was less than one-third the landing distance of a Skymaster, due to it having four wheels with a larger wheel diameter and therefore larger brake discs.

Pitched to retail at a relatively affordable $15,000 (about $87,000 today)— though it probably would end up costing nearer to $30,000—the two parts could be purchased separately (presumably in case one needed a spare pair of wings, as you do…). There were plans for an assembly plant to be located in southern California, once the plane-auto had FAA certification. And by 1973 there was already a car dealer signed up—Galpin Ford—champing at the bit to distribute the vehicles nationally. So far, so good. A lot of thought had gone into this and it all sounded pretty official. What could possibly go wrong?

Grand Unveiling

The AVE Mizar was unveiled in early May 1973 at Van Nuys airport, where ground testing had taken place. (For some strange reason, inventors' follies are not permitted to take flight at metropolitan airports….) Experienced pilot Charles Janisse came on board to carry out a test flight on August 26 at Oxnard Air Force Base (now Camarillo Airport). During the flight he became aware that a locking pin on the right wing had come loose. Sensing that turning the plane in the air would cause the wing to detach, he brought the vehicle down safely in a field then drove it back to base on roads cleared of traffic. This semi-successful flight attracted good publicity for AVE, despite the hitch.

Crash and Burn

The next test flight took place on September 11, 1973, and since pilot Janisse wasn't available inventors Smolinski and Blake took the controls. As air traffic control watched through binoculars, the same issue occurred and the right wing started to detach. The less-experienced pilots did not know they should not turn the plane in these

> ## "…[so easy to assemble that] a woman can easily put the two systems together—or separate them—without help."

—Henry Smolinksi

circumstances—and the wing came off. The flying auto plummeted to the ground, hit a parked pickup truck and burst into a ball of flames (living up to the Pinto's reputation), killing both its inventor-pilots.

Investigations deduced that the wings detached because of dodgy welding combined with the weight of the car plus the pilots making the whole thing far too heavy. Despite the dramatic end to the AVE Mizar's journey (the project was shut down after the crash), the AVE folks should be celebrated for creating a roadable plane that did take off and land on one occasion, unlike attempts by many other inventors. But they perhaps just weren't as advanced as the AVE name suggests when it came to paying attention to detail.

Chapter 2

HAVE YOU THOUGHT THIS THROUGH?

#7 THE CRINOLINE

THE DRESS THAT HIT BELOW THE BELT

1850s | Europe

Gigantic skirts were *de rigueur* for aristocratic women in the nineteenth century. But when the lampshade-style petticoat called a crinoline was invented, it all went a little bit too far.

#7 The Crinoline

In the mid-nineteenth century, women from all walks of life were pretty much consigned to wearing layer upon layer of heavy petticoats to make their skirts swell to an acceptable level in order to achieve that fashionable silhouette with a tiny waist. These petticoats were hot, heavy, and cumbersome, and the fabric that was used to line the skirts to puff them out and create the sought-after, bell-shaped look was stiffened horsehair—itchy! The fabric was known as crinoline, from the French word for horsehair "*crin.*"

Skirting Around the Subject

In order to solve the problem of multiple layers of heavy skirts, people began making cages out of whatever they could find—cane, whalebone, even inflatable rubber tubes that maids puffed up with bellows for the unlucky wearer. None of these were viable solutions, though. Cane snapped easily, whalebone was inflexible and painful, and the rubber was very smelly from the chemical used in production, as well as having a tendency to collapse or burst. One design even allowed the wearer to deflate it in order to sit down, though she'd have to carry bellows around in order to reinflate it, of course!

Little is known about the French inventor called R. C. Milliet who came to women's rescue with a relatively lightweight, flexible, steel-framed hoop skirt, which took the name of the crinoline fabric. Milliet is believed to have been a woman. The invention was patented in Britain in July of 1856, submitted by Milliet under the name Clothide Amet, who may have been Milliet's agent, or coinventor. It was filed as an "Improved means of distending articles of dress and preserving the form or shape thereof." This followed Milliet first patenting an elastic hooped skirt design in France a few months earlier.

Milliet's invention was rigid enough to hold several pounds' worth of heavy dress fabric in a puffball shape, but, ingeniously, it was also flexible as it had steel springs fastened with tape, so the dress could bend inward a little if pushing up against something or sitting down (good luck with that) before popping back into shape. It also made the skirt swing lightly and more freely, making it a little easier to sit down (though the wearer would selfishly take up a whole couch). And the space that the steel-framed crinoline created allowed women more freedom of movement to walk compared to previous versions.

But it also had the effect of revealing rather too much if a lady bent over slightly, such as when climbing stairs, as her whole hoop frame sprung upward, showing her long drawers. Shockingly, the swaying design of the frame also revealed ladies' ankles when they walked, much to the delight of many gentlemen at the time. The voluminous, tent-like nature of the skirt had the added bonus of making it the perfect disguise for smuggling counterfeit goods over borders, or for hiding a lover if caught in the act, so to speak.

So, the steel-framed crinoline took off. By the end of the decade factories had churned out thousands of the hoop frames for Americans, Brits, and other Europeans.

Nerves of Steel

Before we get caught up in "crinolinemania," as *Punch* magazine called it at the time, let us stop to consider the risks of this seemingly wonderful invention. A skirt that's 15–18 feet (4.5–5.5 m) wide does tend to be difficult to maneuver. At the less risky end of the scale, crinolines would cause passersby to trip over or the wearer to knock over anything and everything in their way (including expensive ceramics and furniture). There were even reports of women being blown into the path of passing carriages if a strong gust of wind caught the underside of the skirt.

The fashion for huge crinolines came at a much higher price, though, for the thousands of women who burned to death—for the skirts covering the frame were highly flammable. The huge girth of the skirts and the flexible design of the frame meant one wrong step and the skirt would swing into an open fire and go up in flames. Putting out the flames was pretty difficult as the steel-framed wearer couldn't exactly roll on the ground or smother the flames with a rug. A disaster occurred in 1863 in a church in Santiago, Chile, when a fire spread rapidly thanks in part to the high crinoline count from the 2,000–3,000 women in the congregation, who died. Not only did their skirts act as kindling, but the large hoop frames made escape from the building very difficult.

As fashions go, the crinoline is up there with corsets and foot-binding. It was considered progress at the time, but it had died out by the 1870s. All is forgiven, stiletto heels.

Woodcut illustration showing that fashion can get you hot under the collar, from a pamphlet warning against wearing crinolines.

#8 SMELL-O-VISION

WHEN MOVIES SET OUT TO BE STINKERS

1960 | Hollywood, California

You're relaxing at the movies. Want to smell the alcohol fumes released by a smashed barrel of wine? Or the pipe-tobacco "scent" of a sinister character? We thought not.

#8 Smell-O-Vision

This was a time when TV was becoming popular. Entertainment was available at home, and movie studios were desperate for features—and, dare we say it, gimmicks—that would convince members of the public to continue going to the movies. Smell-O-Vision was a technical system designed to release odors into a movie theater at crucial moments of a film's plot. Designed by Swiss-born inventor Hans Laube and developed in cooperation with Mike Todd, Jr., son of a more famous movie-producer father of the same name, it crashed and burned on its release as part of the film *Scent of Mystery* in 1960.

Battle of the Smellies

Smell-O-Vision must have seemed like a good idea at the time. For one thing, various producers and entrepreneurs had been trying to develop a version of the same idea for years—the great Walt Disney apparently toyed with the idea of including a smell-as-you-watch element in his classic *Fantasia* (1940) but gave up because of the costs involved. Plus which, a rival version of the same idea with the rather better name of AromaRama was being rushed to market at the very time that *Scent of Mystery* was set for release. The AromaRama film was a travelogue about China called *Behind the Great Wall*. Opening on December 2, 1959, it beat *Scent of Mystery* to the screen by a few weeks. The contest between the two films was dubbed "Battle of the Smellies" by *Variety* magazine.

Introducing the Smell Brain

Smell-O-Vision involved kitting out the entire movie theater at a cost of up to $1 million ($8.5 million in today's money). Vents for the release of the scents were installed beneath the moviegoers' seats. The system worked using a "smell brain," a device linked to the movie projector that operated a set of containers of different perfumes. As the film ran through the projector, it set the "smell brain" running, and this pricked the covers of the perfume containers, releasing the scents they contained. Fans then blew the scents through the vents beneath the seats in the theater.

Have You Thought This Through?

Scent of Mystery was directed by famous cinematographer Jack Cardiff (who worked on films including *Black Narcissus* and *The Red Shoes*) and starred no lesser figures than Peter Lorre, Elizabeth Taylor, and Denholm Elliot. And the "smell brain" was a star, too: after a wine barrel fell off a wagon the scent of grapes was pumped into the theater; the presence of the killer was associated with the odor of pipe tobacco.

Too complicated, you say? The system certainly had teething problems. The release from the vents made a distracting hissing noise. Not all members of the audience got their smell hit at the same time—people in the balcony reported smelling the scent several seconds after they were supposed to and after the action of the film had moved on. Others felt they didn't smell it at all—or not strongly enough—and there were complaints about some audience members distracting others by making loud sniffing noises.

German scratch and sniff card for the film Polyester. *The card says:* "Please wait. Do not rub until the number in the movie flashes."

Whiff of Failure

Scent of Mystery was shown with a short film called *Old Whiff*, which told the story of a bloodhound whose sense of smell had gone missing. Even the fact that the dog was voiced by Bert Lahr, famous as the Cowardly Lion in the immortal 1939 picture *The Wizard of Oz*, could not save this doomed double bill. Maybe the moviegoers rather envied the dog who had been set free from all the fuss about smelling.

Neither Smell-O-Vision nor AromaRama proved popular. It could be that filmgoers just didn't want their sense of smell involved in the movie-going experience. There were negative reviews in the *New Yorker*, *Variety*, and *The New York Times*. Both systems flopped; *Scent of Mystery* was renamed *Holiday in Spain* and released without its scents.

But it's just possible the problem was not the idea itself so much as the technical issues. Years later cult moviemaker John Waters paid homage to the smellies when he released his 1981 film *Polyester* in what he called Odorama. Waters was a bit more low-tech, though. Audience members were given scratch and sniff cards and instructed to release the smells imprinted in the cards by rubbing them at key moments on the film. A message popped up on screen with a number from one to ten matching the numbers on the cards. The smells included pizza (OK), gas and glue (are you sure?), and feces (yuk). One of the best things about the *Polyester* version was the ad line: "It'll blow your nose!" Perhaps there's a future for more smells at the movies, after all?

> "I didn't understand the picture. I had a cold."

—Henny Youngman, comedian

#9 THE ILLUMINATED TIRE
TRAVELING LIGHT

1961 | Akron, Ohio

Drivers could have lit up the roads of the United States with Goodyear illuminated tires. But this bright idea didn't take dust and dirt into account...

#9 The Illuminated Tire

The Golden Age of the 1950s was filled with style—and, dare we say it, decadence. The decade certainly had its flaws, but there was much to celebrate in the booming economy. By the end of the 1950s, many families were living in their own houses, owning their own cars, and accessorizing everything they could with new inventions.

Then, in the very early 1960s, consumers were finding themselves with money burning holes in their pockets and companies were more than happy to find ways to help them spend it. People were leaning into all sorts of fads, not least car aficionados. Personal vehicles were moving away from the traditional cookie-cutter designs into an age of individuality. It wasn't just the designs of the car shapes that were evolving; everything inside and outside was also being improved.

In 1961, the Goodyear Tire & Rubber Company was feeling creative. They wanted to make "The Tire of Tomorrow." They had employees brainstorming different kinds of materials and customizations. They hoped their products would help them to stand out from the rest of the companies, which were also busy innovating.

Reinventing the Wheel

Chemist William Larson and his colleague Anthony Finelli were playing around with various ideas. The innovation they came up with was a polyurethane compound that could be dyed all sorts of different colors. Car nuts today might identify "whitewall" tires as a cool accessory, but Goodyear was thinking way out of the box at this point. The two inventors presented the idea to their higher-ups and the company was amped about the customization. Drivers could change the color of their tires as easily as they could change a pair of shoes! Though obviously, more tools were involved.

John J. Hartz, a development manager at the company, is on record saying, "Someday a wife may tell a husband: 'Charlie, go out and change the tires. I'm wearing my blue dress tonight.'" (If that comment doesn't exemplify this time period on all levels, then we're not sure what will.)

Larson and Finelli didn't leave the idea there, though. Because the compound was pretty translucent, it sparked the idea of illuminating the tires to make them even more radiant. To test out their theory, they messed around with lights until they settled on attaching eighteen tiny dash lights to the rim of each tire. They were wired at the center of the wheel to give them power.

Electric Results

Goodyear was ecstatic about the idea. They wanted to gauge the reaction from average car owners, so they put sets on two different models and went out on the town to wow spectators. They sent a Dodge Polar out on the streets of Miami and a Chrysler Silver 300 in New York City to show off the illuminated tires. Passersby going about their nightly business were impressed! Goodyear had a hit. Or so they thought. But that's actually as far as the tires went for the general public, which is… deflating, to say the least.

The major downside of the invention was that the road affected the aesthetic of the tires almost immediately. A quick drive down the block made the tires dirty, blocking their transparent beauty. Plus, the rubber was expensive, as was coming up with a less costly way to keep them electrified. Practicality was not on their side and Goodyear decided against manufacturing them for retail.

One lucky private custom car builder was given a set to display on his own car, however. His name was Jim "Street" Skonzakes and his claim to fame was inventing the Golden Sahara II. He called the Goodyear product "glass tires" and was honored to have them mounted on his unique car. Realistically, with today's technology, it is only a matter of time before LED lights are added to tires and will actually function well. Hint, hint, tire makers. Until then, illuminated tires will only be seen in dreams.

Fantastic Fads

There have been a handful of crazy tire fads throughout the years. In the 1990s, color-changing tire smoke was invented, inspired by the smoke naturally given off by sport drifters' tires while maneuvering corners. The process involved adding a chemical compound (colored specifically) to the rubber of the tire that burned off during impact with the road, releasing vibrant color. It is still popular today and companies forge ahead improving the functionality of this spectacular technology with onlookers cheering the idea on. It should come as no surprise that it is quite expensive but clearly not a dumb invention.

How is this for dumb, though? A crafty man named Jason Winckler tried to make SQUARE tires! Of course, the TV show *MythBusters* strapped regular-sized ones onto a truck and drove around for a while. Seems they only worked when going very fast (and they made for a bumpy ride).

If it makes you feel better, the first lights on automobiles were actual lanterns and they often set everything on fire. Progress?

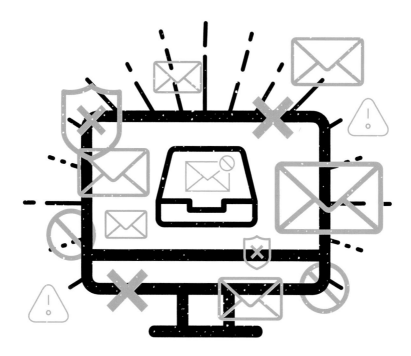

#10 DIGITAL SPAM

THE SPAM THAT CLOGS YOUR INBOX

1978 | Massachusetts

A marketing tool that works? Or a deluge of unwanted information and outlandish begging messages—not to mention the virus-laden links—that stops you from seeing genuine emails?

#10 Digital Spam

Gary Thuerk was a marketer for Digital Equipment Corporation (DEC) computers who decided to use ARPANET (the early version of the internet) to send a message to 393 people in 1978. It was about a demo for a new model of computer, and, like many annoying spammers to come, he wrote it ALL IN CAPS. This, the first documented digital spam message, provoked much the same outrage as the later forms it would spawn, although one man hit reply all (another early instance of an internet *faux pas*) to let people know that at least the demo might be interesting, unlike the birth announcements and other "uninteresting mail" everyone else sends.

Thuerk later recalled: "I thought of it as e-marketing." Though he admitted, "I knew I was pushing the envelope." He added: "We wanted to reach as many people as possible to let them know about our new product." The gimmick worked. Thuerk stated that they sold "$13 million or $14 million worth" of DEC computers off the back of the pioneering campaign.

Spam's Forerunner

Funnily enough, spam was a thing more than a century before the first digital spam message. In 1864, Messrs. Gabriel of 27 Harley Street, London, came up with the idea of sending advertising telegrams about their dental practice to 100 influential and wealthy folks. (Even then, spammers were finding ways to target people!) This inventive yet outrageous act caused an uproar and even incited one British politician to write to *The Times* of London to complain about the "intolerable nuisance": "I have never had any dealings with Messrs. Gabriel, and beg to know by what right do they disturb me by a telegram which is simply the medium of advertisement?"

While not called spam, these spammy telegrams became a huge industry—so much so that in 1928, Nelson E. Ross wrote a booklet, *How To Write Telegrams Properly*, describing how to send thousands of telegrams at once for no additional cost. He helpfully mentioned that these telegrams could be used for advertising or for "collections of accounts." Sounds like bill collectors have been harassing people in all mediums for just as long as spammers...

But Why "Spam"?

How did spam get its name? And what did email messages have to do with the potted meat SPAM, introduced in 1937 by the Hormel Food Corp. of Minnesota? The term spam didn't show up definitively until 1993, when Richard Depew accidentally posted the same message 200 times in a row to a newsgroup on Usenet, a bulletin board discussion system. He and others called it spam afterward: "Lovely spam! Wonderful spam!" But to find out where the name spam comes from, we have to go back a few more years, to messages that users sent to each other in the 1980s on multi-user dungeons (MUDs), a kind of a primitive version of *World of Warcraft* or *Second Life*, where people could interact with each other in shared environments.

Certain users would "spam" the chats with files and chunks of text meant to disrupt, in a similar way to how "trolls" antagonize others online nowadays. Often, these chunks of text would be the words to a song by British comedy troupe Monty Python—about the potted meat SPAM written as part of a TV sketch in 1970. In it, a waitress recited a list of dishes to a couple of customers, and nearly every dish had SPAM in it: "... egg and spam; egg bacon and spam; egg bacon sausage and spam; spam bacon sausage and spam; spam egg spam spam bacon and spam; spam sausage spam spam bacon spam tomato and spam..." Occasionally, a chorus of Vikings overwhelmed everything by singing: "SPAM! SPAM! SPAM! SPAM! Lovely SPAM! Wonderful SPAM!"

Hormel Puts Up a Fight

Funnily enough, Hormel wasn't thrilled at their tinned meat product possibly being confused with an invention that nobody wanted. For a while, the company tried to fight the association with junk email by attempting to trademark the word "spam." They lost the trademark bid because a judge pointed out that it was a useful term for something that affects a lot of people—and it would be pretty hard to get everyone to start calling it something else. Hormel's official position is now that it doesn't object to calling unsolicited emails spam—it just wants us all to write SPAM in all caps when we're talking about salty pork in the shape of a can. (And we all know that all caps is only annoying online, right?)

"SPAM! SPAM! SPAM!
SPAM! Lovely SPAM!
Wonderful SPAM!"

—Monty Python

#11 THE POP-UP AD

PERSISTENT POP-UPS THAT DRIVE WEB USERS CRAZY

1990s | Massachusetts

The idea wasn't bad—but the experience was. Online pop-up ads were born as a clever marketing tool but became a plague hated by internet users.

#11 The Pop-Up Ad

Pop-up ads were invented in the late 1990s by Ethan Zuckerman and his team at Tripod.com, a marketing company, webpage host, and social network site at the time. Zuckerman used details on his users' websites to create ads specifically tailored to them and their visitors. He started by slapping the advertising directly onto the page. But when a major car company complained after a banner ad for its products featured on a webpage devoted to... shall we say, grown-up fun-time activities, the company made it plain, in no uncertain terms, it was unimpressed.

Arm's Length Advertisements

Zuckerman needed to find a way of placing advertising where the target consumer would see it, without directly associating the advertising with the webpage the consumer was visiting. So, he and his team figured, what if a new page opened automatically? The ad would still appear, but it would be separate. It wouldn't look as if it was actually a part of the website. Zuckerman wrote the code for the world's first pop-up ad.

By magically appearing in a new window, the luxury car commercial found its target audience without looking like it was specifically a brand of automobile designed with... people who enjoy watching grown-up fun-time activity videos in mind. Not that there is anything wrong with that, of course. But you have to question the welcome afforded to a magically appearing commercial for SUVs suddenly manifesting itself in the middle of your... screen.

Writing in *The Atlantic* in 2014, Zuckerman explained that the outfit was advertising-funded and its USP, so to speak, was its ability to analyze users' homepages so as to better target ads. He recalled of the new form of advertisement: "It was a way to associate an ad with a user's page without putting it directly on the page, which advertisers worried would imply an association between their brand and the page's content." He added: "We ended up creating one of the most hated tools in the advertiser's toolkit: the pop-up ad... I'm sorry. Our intentions were good."

Cold Callers?

Pop-up ads—undeniably a cute marketing ploy—soon really grated with internet users. Advertisements can be irritating when they interrupt your favorite radio show or TV drama, but the timing of those ads is at least predictable. Pop-ups were on a different level—bursting onto the screen, diverting your attention, blocking the view, interrupting your reading. What's more, the feelings they generated toward whatever people were reading could be negative.

They were like the online equivalent of cold-callers at your front door—uninvited guests barging in and trying to sell you something while placing themselves directly between you and the thing you were doing at the time; or like a wandering Mariachi band on a restaurant terrace—a jarring intrusion that demands attention and stops you enjoying your day.

> "We ended up creating one of the most hated tools in the advertiser's toolkit: the pop-up ad... I'm sorry. Our intentions were good."

—Ethan Zuckerman

... And Clickbait

Zuckerman's invention took on a life of its own. The even uglier sister of the pop-up ad arrived in the form of the pop-up clickbait ad. These started to appear randomly, wanting to take consumers away to another website with promises of a seven-day way to lose belly fat, or the secret to how a woman makes $6,000 a day while relaxing with a piña colada in a hammock in Bermuda. If Zuckerman's pop-ups were unwanted visitors on the doorstep, clickbait pop-ups were kidnappers who throw a bag over your head, bundle you into an unmarked van, and take you to an unknown destination from which you may never be able to navigate your way home.

Pop-ups still exist in some of the darker corners of the internet but are nowhere near as pervasive as they once were. This is largely due to fightback headed by browsers Netscape and Opera, who were actually the first to add pop-up blockers to their product in the early 2000s. These days, most browsers employ blocking technology. That isn't the end of the conversation, though. Both advertisers and web providers that rely on advertising money to operate are less than delighted about the consumers' ability to block ads. The internet is mostly free because the users are the product, sold by content providers to advertisers. Fans of free internet must embrace the ads in one way or another—just not during dinner.

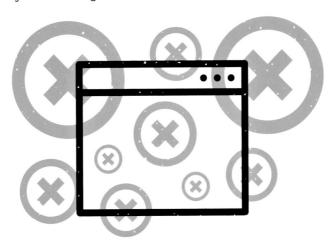

#12 COMIC SANS

THE WORLD'S MOST HATED FONT

1994 | Redmond, Washington

The font that has infected the typographic world has shown up everywhere, from bake sale flyers to papal tributes. This cheery font now attracts widespread derision, but it was never meant to be that way...

#12 Comic Sans

The violently disliked Comic Sans font was created by Vincent Connare, a Microsoft "typographic engineer," in 1994 for a project he stumbled into at work titled Microsoft Bob. (Microsoft Bob deserves his own chapter on inventions that never should have happened. He was like Clippy on speed, taking over your whole computer, possibly your whole life.) The program, scheduled to ship with Windows 95, included a lot of speech bubbles including some from cartoon dog "Rover" to guide baffled people through using their computers. (This was in the olden days, when the majority of people were still computer noobs.) The type in the speech bubbles was the more formal Times New Roman. Connare professed: "I thought, 'That's silly. Dogs don't talk like that.' So I said it would look better if it looked like a comic book." He set about designing a font fit for canines. (Connare also designed the Trebuchet font, among others.)

He took his inspiration from comic books in his office—specifically Alan Moore's *Watchmen* and Frank Miller's *The Dark Knight Returns*—to create the rounded, childlike typeface. It was only ever supposed to be used in Microsoft Bob's interface, but the typeface wasn't finished in time to be shipped with Windows 95. Instead, Microsoft would later use it in 3D Movie Maker and eventually add it to their standard fonts, so the font is now shipped with just about every computer in the world.

Font of Strong Feelings

Comic Sans inspired a "Ban Comic Sans" campaign, sites like Comic Sans in the Wild that collected inappropriate uses of the typeface, a Flash-based shooting game called Kill Comic Sans, and an April Fool's Day browser extension that converted all text to Comic Sans. Of course, it had its fans, too. McSweeney's published a hilarious, inspired piece by Mike Lacher from the point of view of the despondent font and included gems like: "I am a sans serif Superman and my only kryptonite is pretentious buzzkills like you." For all the good reasons out there to dislike Comic Sans, it does have one saving grace: It's easier to read for people with dyslexia.

Have You Thought This Through?

There are a lot of analyses out there about why we all feel so strongly about Comic Sans, but it seems to boil down to two main points. First, the technical things like kerning and weighting of the font are inconsistent. Second, people just use it inappropriately. Before Windows 95, most people didn't have access to desktop publishing. But suddenly, they could make their own posters and flyers—and they could use any font they wanted! It still hadn't gotten that bad, however, because people mostly used it for things like birthday party invitations and Christmas cards. But then the internet went and got more popular. And people still didn't know how to wield the power of Comic Sans properly. It started showing up everywhere— business emails, blogs, and websites. It infected everything.

Font of Inappropriateness

In 2010, NBA owner Dan Gilbert wrote a long rant aimed at LeBron James when he announced he was leaving Cleveland for Miami. The fact that he wrote it in Comic Sans got almost as much attention as the bizarre and hysterical content of the letter. In 2012, a German memorial for World War II troops gained some attention when it was decided that Comic Sans was the right typeface for the words engraved on the stone. When Pope Benedict XVI retired in 2013, the Vatican posted a sixty-page photo album online highlighting his time in office—captioned entirely in Comic Sans.

Connare, who designed it in the first place, is still proud of his ubiquitous work. "You can't go anywhere without seeing Comic Sans," Connare said. (I'm currently writing this in Palatino. Note to editor: Please don't publish this in Comic Sans.)

"Crocs of the font world."

—User responses to Comic Sans font

When to Use Comic Sans

Stuff for kids.

Comics.

When Not to Use Comic Sans

Don't use it in your office. Ever.

Don't use it at funerals.

Don't use it on arrest warrants.

Don't use it on business cards.

Don't use it on your marriage license.

Don't use it on that sign you're going to hang in the
entrance of your apartment building about not dumping trash.

Don't use it for a Vatican tribute to the Pope, Higgs Boson
presentations, or rants by basketball team owners about LeBron James.

Be safe—just don't use it.

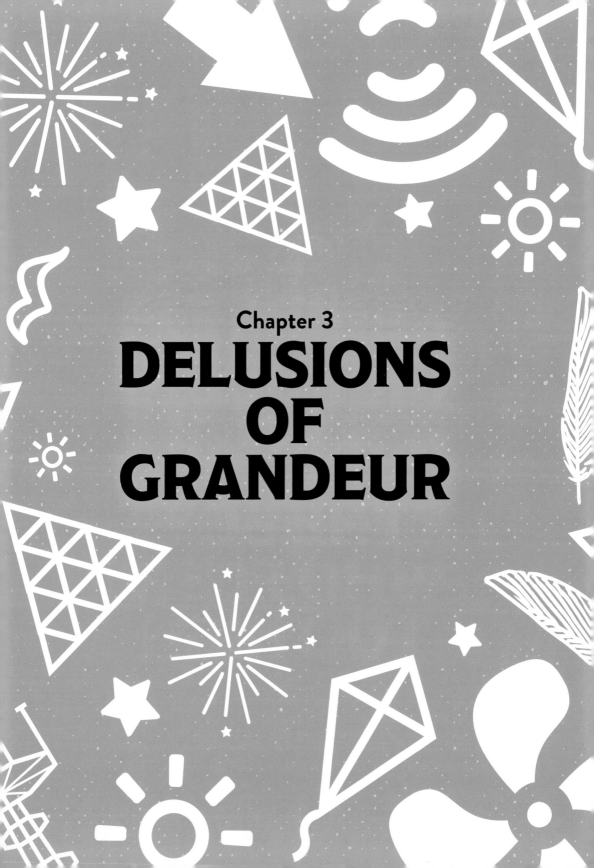

Chapter 3

DELUSIONS OF GRANDEUR

#13 HOMEMADE WINGS
THE BOY WHO FLEW TOO HIGH

~2,000 BCE | Ancient Greece

Icarus soared for a few glorious moments but aimed too high—
and plunged to his death. If only he had listened to Dad, right?

#13 Homemade Wings

Ill-fated inventions aren't just for real life. Long, long before Orville and Wilbur Wright took to the sky on the coast of North Carolina in 1903, Ovid and other ancient poets gave flight to the myth of Icarus, whose winged jaunt was cut short by his lofty ambitions. Icarus may be the one whose name is more often remembered—he even has a psychological complex named after him—but his dad, Daedalus, was the brains behind the invention, according to myth.

Daedalus was quite the craftsman, and he was asked by King Minos of Crete to create a labyrinth to imprison a minotaur. What happens next depends on which version of the myth you read. In one, Daedalus upset Minos by helping Theseus find the center of the maze, while in another, Daedalus was ready to leave and Minos simply didn't want to lose such a skilled craftsman. Whatever the reason, Daedalus and his son, Icarus, were imprisoned by the king.

According to *Metamorphoses* (Ovid's fifteen-book magnum opus of 8 CE), the inventor thought about how to escape. "'He may thwart our escape by land or sea,' he said, 'but the sky is surely open to us: we will go that way: Minos rules everything but he does not rule the heavens.'" So he set to work gathering up feathers, wax, and bits of string, which he used to fashion two sets of wings for him and his son. Like a nervous father turning over the keys to the car for the first time, Daedalus gave Icarus a bunch of last-minute instructions before take-off: Don't fly too close to the Sun and melt the wax, and don't fly too close to the ocean and weigh down the feathers with ocean spray.

Like many teenagers who would come after him, Icarus ignored his father's advice. They both took off, flapping their wings like birds, and it seemed like the invention was working! However, caught up in the wonder of flying, Icarus swooped higher and higher, until the Sun melted his wings and he fell from the sky. Daedalus flew ahead and did not see it happen. "He caught sight of the feathers on the waves, and cursed his inventions," Ovid wrote.

Artist's impression of Icarus crashing to Earth, having not listened to his father.

#13 Homemade Wings

Grains of Truth

Like all myths and stories, there is often a grain of truth in the telling. Daedalus was likely a real artisan and inventor, or a name given to several people whose achievements were later attributed to one man. (The word "*daidalos*" in Greek meant "finely-worked" and "elaborate.") More than 600,000 people a year visit ruins at Knossos in current-day Greece, which many believe are the site of King Minos' palace and a labyrinth that inspired the legend. Surviving frescoes in the ruins show bulls and other images from the myth. And the Icarian Sea is a real body of water off of the island of Crete, where Icarus supposedly drowned.

So, if all of those pieces of the myth could be true, what about the wings? Take it with a pinch of salt, according to MIT engineers. Humans simply don't have the muscle mass to flap our arms with wings attached and actually be able to take off. Your legs might do it, but the wingspan would have to be at least 80 feet (24 m). And you'd probably look pretty stupid flapping your legs like wings...

Should Icarus Have Flown Higher?

Had Daedalus figured out how to bypass physics, flying too close to the Sun wouldn't actually have been the fatal mistake that would have killed Icarus, according to some modern students with a lot of time on their hands and a research paper to write. They did some calculations involving the melting point of wax, the Sun's strength near the equator, and how big the wings would need to be for human flight—and determined that the Sun could have melted Icarus' wings in somewhere between 42 and 67 minutes. And that time wouldn't have changed, no matter how close Icarus was to the Sun, because the Sun is so far away to begin with. Turns out, Icarus might have done better to fly a lot closer to the Sun! Because the higher you go, the colder the atmosphere gets—which might have kept the wax of his wings from melting. Maybe Dad doesn't always know best!

#14 DA VINCI'S WATER-WALKING SHOES

WALKING... IN THE FOOTSTEPS OF JESUS

ca. 1490 | Italy

Da Vinci: one of the greatest geniuses of all time.
But even geniuses have off days.

#14 Da Vinci's Water-walking Shoes

Look up Renaissance Man on the internet and it's most likely Leonardo da Vinci's name that you'll see. This is the guy who painted the *Mona Lisa* and *The Last Supper*. He thought up solar power in the 1400s—something that you and I are only recently seeing pop up on roofs in the neighborhood. And he sketched plans for parachutes, tanks, and helicopters at a time when they were all but impossible to build. Renaissance moms may have been asking their sons why they couldn't be more like that smart young man da Vinci with all the brilliant ideas, but that doesn't mean he didn't churn out a few clunkers, too. At the top of that list is a sketch of what he called "water shoes," found in the *Codex Atlanticus*, a twelve-volume set of his works housed in Milan, Italy.

Walking on Water

In the late fifteenth century, Da Vinci sketched water-walking shoes that looked like snowshoes crossed with cross-country skis. The plan called for inflatable floats made of animal skins to be strapped to the feet, while hand-held poles on similar floats helped to balance and propel the person over the water. In theory. The (mostly) brilliant inventor, who was at one point a military architect and engineer in Venice, was always looking for ways to defend against naval attacks. He apparently believed these floating marvels would help soldiers maneuver around ships and cross moats— although you have to wonder how he thought they'd hold weapons with a walking pole in each hand. He never bothered to hand his beer to a friend while he tried them out.

But modern attempts to build Da Vinci's invention that might have enabled him to walk on water show it never would have left the ground. It is hard to balance on the shoes, let alone cross moats with them. To be fair, though, Da Vinci likely quickly scrawled the drawing without a lot of thought—it's found among grocery lists and records of who owes him money in the thousands of pages of notes he made over his lifetime. Who hasn't woken in the middle of the night and written a weird idea down that makes no sense the next morning?

Control Issues

Fevered dream or not, Da Vinci was probably not just thinking about military applications when he sketched his idea for water-walking shoes. He was more than a little obsessed with water—how it works, and how to control it. His notes were filled with imagery of great floods and storms, of cities and farmhouses being swirled away by roiling waters. (And it's no wonder he seemed a bit scared—he saw the Arno River flood badly more than once in his life.) In his quest to gain power over water, he also came up with ideas for a diving suit, a breathing device similar to a snorkel, webbed swimming gloves, a boat that could travel underwater (500 years before the first submarine was built), bridges that could be carried in case of natural disaster, and locks to control water flow in rivers and canals. While these are all in modern use now, another idea that didn't have quite the same mileage involved troops digging trenches to try to direct the Arno River to flood Pisa. (The Arno did not cooperate.)

More Wishful Water Walkers

Many others have continued to float the idea of devices that will let you walk on water. "Human Water Spider" Charles Oldrieve strolled down the Hudson River in 1888 on a pair of watertight shoes made of cedar and copper plating. In 1975, Walter Robinson walked 52 miles (80 km) through the Panama Canal on his own water shoes invention, then crossed the 22 miles (35 km) of the English Channel in 1978. He tested his fiberglass and plastic-foam shoes, attached to the feet with elastic bands, and found they let you fish, fire a rifle, and throw a football from them (handy). Inventor Yoav Rosen has more than one patent for an "Upright Human Floatation Apparatus and Propulsion Mechanism." It includes two Styrofoam pontoons connected with a cable that lets you basically cross-country ski along the surface of the water. It worked, but Rosen wasn't able to attract funders, so he switched to paddle sports. His kayaks and boats, which sell for thousands of dollars today, get their stability from a double-hulled design—another idea from Da Vinci.

Da Vinci demonstrating that using water shoes would be a walk in the park.

#15 THE ROCKET CHAIR
GOING UP WITH A BANG

Possibly 1500s | China

A rocket scientist needs intelligence, technical knowhow, and the "hi-est" of hi-tech equipment—better not pin your hopes on homemade rockets lit by handheld candles, then!

#15 The Rocket Chair

Chinese court official Wan Hu was determined to achieve fame as the first man to launch himself into space. He was brave as well as driven and savvy—willing to risk his life in pursuit of an almost unimaginable achievement. He was pushing science on and happy, no doubt, to accept the renown that would follow.

"Fire Medicine"

The probably apocryphal story of Wan Hu tells that he was well versed in his countrymen's discovery of gunpowder and development of rockets. Alchemists in China were trying to find an elixir of life—a drink that could make you stay young forever—when they accidentally made the first gunpowder. The scientists called it "fire medicine," but their compatriots quickly saw that it could be used for other purposes such as to fire rockets and burning arrows in warfare. Around the same time, it is believed they may have also invented the first fireworks.

Wan Hu, meanwhile, saw gunpowder's potential to make him the first person to leave the confines of Earth and travel among the Moon and stars. His spaceship consisted of a simple wicker chair suspended between two very long kites set out in parallel. Attached beneath the kites were forty-seven bamboo rockets containing the recently invented "fire medicine." Another account had it that the chair, as illustrated, had the rockets directly attached to it.

The launch was a big event, with an invited audience. Wan turned up in his finest clothes and twirling his moustache, perhaps a little too confident that all would be well. He had forty-seven courtiers lined up to assist. As he clambered into the chair and settled himself, no doubt he looked forward to achieving immortality as China's—the world's—first astronaut? He gave a sign and each of the courtiers lit his candle. Then they moved forward and a hush fell over the invited crowd of the great and good. Each courtier lit his fuse and then all dashed away to take cover. The silence was tense. The seconds ticked by, as all waited for the rockets to fire.

"Houston, We Have a Problem..."

"Ten, nine, eight..." We're all familiar with the space-age countdown and the confident excitement around the launchpad at a modern center like Cape Canaveral in Florida or the Sriharikota launchpad in India. But what happened at Wan Hu's launch was more "Houston, we have a problem" than "We have lift-off!"

"Five, four, three, two, one..." Wan was lost in a mighty cloud of smoke and a huge explosion. And when the smoke cleared, he was nowhere to be seen. Did this mean he had been launched unstoppably upward and was now flying somewhere high above China? Some claimed so, but other—probably more reliable—reports had it that the remains of his chair and his badly burned corpse were found just a few yards from the launchpad.

Could Wan Hu's contraption ever have worked? Modern scientists have tried to recreate his wicker-chair spaceship. A 2004 edition of the TV show *MythBusters* decided that miniature rockets of the kind described would not be powerful enough to provide lift-off for a chair holding a person. In their test run, carried out using materials of the kind Wan Hu would have had available to him, the chair exploded and the "crash dummy" standing in for the Chinese space pioneer was badly burned and flung to the ground.

Wan's ambition overreached his knowledge and technical resources—and he was hundreds of years ahead of history. In particular his reliance on makeshift equipment meant his fearless attempt was doomed to failure.

You could say his wish for immortality was granted all too literally, in that he was blasted through a fiery death into the afterlife. But in another way he did achieve the immortality he craved. His name endures on the dark side of the Moon—the side that is always turned away from the Earth and so cannot be seen from the ground but which has been photographed by NASA's *Apollo 16* and studied by space scientists.

One of the many craters on its surface was named Wan Hoo (using a slightly different spelling of his name) in his honor. And at the Yionang Satellite Center in China this sadly misguided space pioneer is reportedly commemorated with a statue.

Painting of Wan Hu taking off in his rocket chair
(before it exploded, presumably).

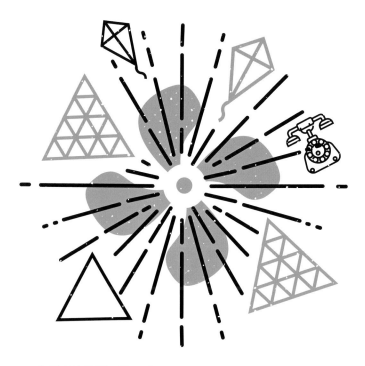

#16 THE CYGNET FLYING KITE

THE IDEA THAT NEVER TOOK OFF

c.1907 | Canada

The race for powered flight drew together some of the greatest minds, cleverest designers, and bravest people on Earth. Alexander Graham Bell? Not so much...

#16 The Cygnet Flying Kite

Alexander Graham Bell is not the first name that comes to mind when the invention of flying machines is brought up. He will forever be known for his pioneering work on the invention of the telephone. But he tried to get his name atop the roster of aviation pioneers with his—ultimately disastrous—Cygnet flying kite.

Bell grew up in Edinburgh, Scotland's capital. His mother became increasingly deaf in his youth and he became interested in acoustics and amplification. His family moved to Canada in 1870, when he was twenty-three. In 1876 he offered to sell his telephone patent to Western Union for $100,000. The company's president, William Orton, baulked, calling the device a "toy." Two years later Orton told colleagues if he could buy the patent for $25 million he would consider it a bargain.

Ring Ring—Kerching!

A few years after that, Bell and his investors were very, very rich. They literally owned the American telephone system. But Alexander didn't stop there. He was a tireless worker. He produced an early wireless phone and medical devices to aid breathing, and his work with magnetic fields produced prototypes that many years later would lead to tape recorders and computer hard disks. In 1881, when US president James Garfield was shot, Bell produced a metal detector to find the bullet. It worked well in testing but not, sadly, in practice. Possibly because the wounded president was lying on a metal bed on a mattress filled with metal wire…

By the 1890s Bell was working on hydrofoils and flying machines. He formed a team—the Aerial Experiment Association—that included motorcycle designer Glenn Curtiss and Bell's fearless pilot, Lieutenant Thomas Selfridge. He wasn't the only inventor in the race to produce the first flying machine. In Europe and the United States, great minds and daredevils were working night and day to be the first to leave the ground. But while most prototypes followed the principles of birds, with wings and a central part where the pilot sits, Bell went another way.

The Birds and the... Boxes

Kites. Bell became obsessed with them. He built them in all sorts of experimental shapes before deciding that tetrahedral was the way to go. Strong and simple, the pyramid shape formed the basic cell that allowed him to build ever-larger kites. One of which, a kite he called "The Frost King," accidentally lifted one of his assistants 30 feet (9 m) in the air in a wind of just 10 mph (16 kmph).

Bell reasoned that a bigger kite, capable of carrying not just a person but also an engine that could provide 10 mph thrust would be, in essence, a self-containing flying machine! In the early 1900s, Bell and his team would labor tirelessly to get such a kite airborne.

The wedge-shaped Cygnet contained 3,393 cells, each a tiny box kite. The pilot, the intrepid Lieutenant Selfridge, would crawl into a tunnel in the middle of the wedge in front of the Curtiss-made engine. The Cygnet was 52 feet (16 m) wide and 10 feet (3 m) high, the 3,393 cells featuring sails made of red silk. Underneath were fitted pontoon floats and it would be launched from the water. Towed, pilotless and engineless behind a steam ship, the Cygnet rose into the air on its first test flight in 1907. Emboldened by this success, Lieutenant Selfridge crawled into his tunnel and, still without the motor fitted, they went for a second launch.

You Had One Lousy Job...

The Cygnet soared 200 feet (60 m) into the air behind the steam-powered boat. An exhilarated Selfridge began his descent. Unfortunately, he couldn't see very well from his tunnel and he hit the water quite hard. Equally unfortunately, he forgot to release the tow rope and the Cygnet was dragged through the water and smashed to pieces. Lieutenant Selfridge escaped unharmed and the project was more or less abandoned at that point.

By the time Bell and his team had spent four years getting their wicker contraption off the ground, the Wright Brothers had pretty much invented the airplane. His idea, perhaps more than a little misguided, had missed its moment. Bell moved on. In 1915 he said: "I have no doubt that a machine will be driven from the Earth's surface at enormous velocities by a new method of propulsion—think of tremendous energies locked up in explosives—what if we could utilize these in projectile flight?" Yes, that's right. To his credit, he wasn't far off envisaging the modern space rocket.

Staring contest between Bell and a woman inside a prototype of his Cygnet flying kite. (She won and didn't have to fly in it.)

#17 THE PARACHUTE SUIT

ONE GIANT FALL FOR HUMANKIND...

1912 | Paris, France

Franz Reichelt had complete confidence in the gravity-
defying powers of his homemade parachute suit.
But it let him down... and down...

#17 The Parachute Suit

In the early twentieth century, Austrian-born tailor Franz Reichelt was operating a successful dressmaking business in Paris. But parachutes were his real love. He set himself the task of creating a flying suit for aviators that doubled as a parachute in case of emergency, and by 1912 he was ready to test it.

It had been quite a challenge. The death rate for pilots was pretty high, since no working parachute for use in airplanes existed—though others had successfully tested canopies for use from hot-air balloons. Reichelt constructed a wearable frame with rods and a hooded, silk canopy around the head and arms, giving a batwing effect and reminiscent of a puppet-show tent. There was also a rubber fold-out element that deployed a wider, functional parachute of approximately 100 square feet (9 sq m) in area. If it deployed, that is.

In its casual, strolling-to-the-airplane mode, the parachute suit was not much bigger than a standard aviator's overalls, with the doohickeys all neatly folded into a built-in knapsack, ready to transform into the hooded wonder-cape with just a stretch out of the arms into a crucifix shape. The inventor ran successful tests with dummies dropped out of his apartment window, but the designs that evolved from these early prototypes didn't work very well (read: at all). Next he bravely tried the suit out himself from a height of around 32 feet (10 m) but broke a leg in the process. He remained undeterred. His unwavering self-belief, his desire to be remembered, and his insistence that a higher drop would make the design work led him to put heavy pressure on the Paris police prefecture for permission to do a test flight, throwing a suited-up dummy off the Eiffel Tower.

The Big Drop

The police finally agreed to a dummy drop on February 4, 1912. So Reichelt sent out a press release about the experiment, building the event up for the Paris paparazzi in the hope of securing sponsorship in order to make a profit on his design. On a chilly, breezy February morning, much to everyone's surprise, Reichelt arrived kitted out in his elaborate contraption, desperate to show his doubters and the media that his invention worked. At this point it became apparent that Reichelt was going to attempt the nearly 200-foot (60-m) jump himself. He'd invested time and money in getting every little detail right, so it was a no-brainer—he may have felt—that he should be the one to perform the inaugural test flight and showcase his revolutionary innovation. He had his impressive, Stalinesque handlebar mustache suitably primped and preened for the occasion.

He told journalists that he wouldn't be taking any safety precautions (such as a safety rope) as he knew his parachute would work. He said: "I want to try the experiment myself and without trickery, as I intend to prove the worth of my invention." Fellow inventor Gaston Hervieu tried to dissuade him, but Reichelt replied: "You are going to see how my seventy-two kilos [159 lb] and my parachute will give your arguments the most decisive of denials."

Into the Void

After adjusting the suit with his friends' help, Reichelt stepped onto the rail, shook his friends' hands, then paused before launching himself over the edge. His last words to the small crowds (it was early in the morning, and cold—what are you going to do?) were "See you soon." The countdown began, his heart beat faster and faster, he took a leap of faith and—plunged down, down, down... The suit wrapped itself around him rather than opening out and he descended quickly to his death, brutally slamming onto the ground.

Major French newspapers covered the story of the mad inventor with haunting black-and-white images of his descent. To add insult to injury, Reichelt's fatal plummet was filmed by journalists and shown on newsreels with stories about the "reckless inventor." His body was efficiently cleared by Paris gendarmes, revealing a Reichelt-shaped crater where he hit the frozen ground. Not the impact the brave inventor had hoped to have, but he did go down in history after all.

Franz Reichelt standing proudly in his "flying suit," 1912.

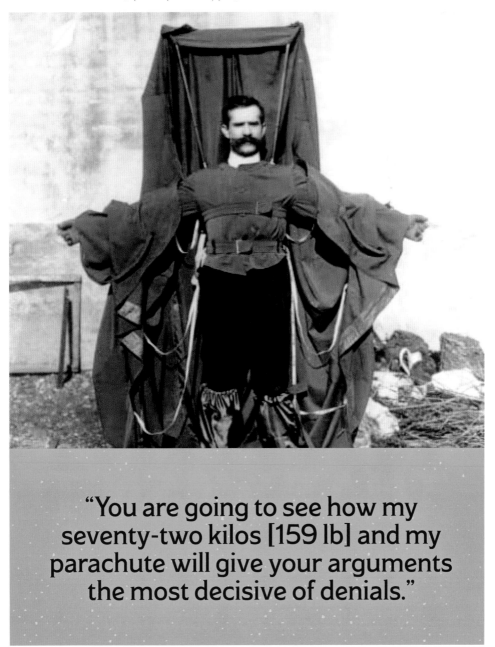

"You are going to see how my seventy-two kilos [159 lb] and my parachute will give your arguments the most decisive of denials."

—Franz Reichelt

#18 THE POCKET TV
THE 2-INCH TV THAT WASN'T

1976 | Cambridge, UK

The master of miniaturization, Clive Sinclair, finally turned his talents to the big one. Or, more accurately, the little one.

#18 The Pocket TV

In the 1970s, Clive Sinclair was already a legend in nerd circles in the UK and much of the world. Tech savvy and always looking to miniaturize, Sinclair designed a pocket transistor radio in the early 1960s, and in 1972 he produced the world's first slimline pocket calculator. The holy grail, though, was always going to be the pocket TV.

In 1976, the pocket TV was both an idea ahead of its time and one that every square-eyed kid on the planet had already dreamed of for at least two decades before it was launched. A portable television! You could watch your favorite shows wherever you want! You could even keep it in your desk at school and watch *Bonanza* in secret while your teacher thinks she is teaching you how to multiply fractions! The concept was not new. The reality, sadly, did not quite live up to the dream. Like when you were expecting a Superman outfit on your sixth birthday and your granny crocheted one for you herself.

There were several brilliant innovations required to make a TV this small, one of which was to redesign the cathode ray tube—essentially a gun firing a beam of electrons at a phosphor coating on the front of the tube that lights up and builds the picture in quickly drawn lines. Sinclair produced a cathode ray tube that was smaller, brighter, and used less power than anything before it.

Brilliant innovations, but sadly soon redundant as the liquid crystal displays appearing in calculators and watches were about to prove a nimbler, lighter, and cheaper solution for small-screen tech. Sinclair's pocket TV was also multi-standard and multi-system. You could take it anywhere in the world and it would pick up and display VHF and UHF signals broadcast by local TV stations. His market was global.

The Great Reveal
In 1976, Sir Clive unveiled his first version, the MTV1 Microvision, and yes—the screen was just 2 inches (5 cm) wide! The problem is the rest of it was… not. It was only a pocket TV if you happened to be a magician, say, or a shoplifter with specialized

garments. If you could produce a rabbit from your sleeve or steal a gallon of pineapple juice and secrete it about your person—this was the pocket TV for you! As well as being generously proportioned, Sir Clive's MTV1 was, well, a little on the weighty side. A shoebox full of house bricks might not be as entertaining but would provide you with a similar workout while jogging.

The aerial required for receiving the broadcasts was equally impressive in stature, and with the release of *Star Wars* just around the corner in 1977, it could easily have doubled as a makeshift lightsaber. And if you imagine just how quickly a lightsaber would get through a set of domestic batteries, then you will have some idea of how thirsty the MTV1 was. The internal batteries were rechargeable, but when Darth Vader is busy slicing open the cockpit door, the wait time may well cause more than a little bit of a frustration.

But to avoid that problem by using non-rechargeable batteries, the average picnic would have you cross-belted like a bandolero with replacement AAs. But wait... you could use it with a mains adaptor! So long as you were happy with your freedom to roam only stretching as far as your extension cord, that is.

Reception Was... Mixed

The TV tuned like an old radio, and, like any portable radio in the 1970s, the process wasn't always going to go smoothly. So as well as trying to obtain good sound reception, you were dealing with moving pictures, which meant that your optimum viewing position could very likely involve standing on a chair. On a table. Outside. Preferably at night. The screen was just about the only successfully miniature thing about it. Which is when we come to the main drawback about mini TVs. Given the choice of watching a 2-inch (5-cm) screen or watching a screen literally any size larger than that, you're going to go with the second option, right?

But let's get down to the important detail: Was it in color? Yes, two. Black and white. Sinclair's MTV1 retailed at around $400, which is up around $1,800 today. That's the price of a couple of top-range iPads. But those were different times. The MTV1, like jetpacks and hoverboards, had been the answer to the dreams of tube-addicted kids for several generations. Granted it wasn't the answer they expected. Not even the answer they wanted, if truth be told. But, as your teacher probably told you (had you been paying attention), there are no wrong answers—only new lessons to be learned.

Clive Sinclair looks super excited about his new pocket TV.

Chapter 4
A BLIP IN HISTORY BEST FORGOTTEN

#19 EDISON'S TALKING DOLL

CUTE? OR JUST PLAIN TERRIFYING?

1890 | New York City, New York

Think of Thomas Edison, and inventions like the phonograph and incandescent lightbulb come to mind. Not Chucky from the film *Child's Play*. But be prepared to be surprised. Or sleepless.

#19 Edison's Talking Doll

Having created the phonograph, inventor Thomas Edison was looking for a way to bring it into every household. He decided the item that could achieve this was a doll for "Nice Little Girls," as one newspaper worded it. The uniqueness of his doll was that it would come with a pre-recorded verse. He founded the Edison Phonograph Toy Manufacturing Company to bring his idea, the Edison Talking Doll, to life.

This execution of the technology was brand-spanking new and exciting for the time. Fun fact: It was recognized as the first known use of recording artists. Young women were employed by the company to sit in cubicles and record different well-known nursery rhymes. Each recording was for a single doll. Duplication hadn't been invented yet. At 22 inches (55 cm) high and weighing in at 4 lb (1.8 kg), the talking doll was equipped with wooden limbs, a tin torso, and a porcelain head, with a miniature version of Edison's phonograph tucked inside her chest cavity. The phonograph was operated by using a crank handle that activated the etched-wax recording.

Bleak

Sounds pretty cool, right? Well, here's where it broke down. First of all, the technology was so new that the recording quality was terrible. The women who recorded the nursery rhymes were essentially shouting these well-known verses into recording devices in a factory setting. Imagine hearing "TWINKLE TWINKLE LITTLE STAR HOW I WONDER WHAT YOU ARE!" yelled at you by a doll. Doesn't sound very soothing, does it?

The reality of owning one was pretty bleak. Add to that the hand-cranking needed to make the phonograph work. The young girls who owned these precious toys would need to keep the rotation at a steady pace. If they didn't, the sounds quickly turned terrifying: It was either too slow, making the doll sound demonic; or too fast, which made the doll frantically pound through the words as though trying to get the job over with as quickly as possible.

Little Monsters

Consumers were also unable to pick the specific recording, so each doll sold was a crapshoot. There is no information on whether or not patrons could test them in the store. Regardless, with only one nursery rhyme per doll, you'd better really enjoy hearing "Mary Had a Little Lamb" over and over and over again because that was all that was going to entertain you. Forever. Or until the mechanism broke. Which was often only a few hours after its arrival at the house. The Edison Talking Dolls were also extremely expensive for the time—$10 for the base model, which was equal to about a week's salary for the average household. And that version was only clothed in a simple chemise. If you wanted a nice dress, it was an extra $10. That, in itself, was somewhat baffling because it equated the cost of the phonograph to that of a fancy dress.

The highly anticipated dolls were shipped to stores in April 1890. Initially customers clamored to buy them. But once people got them home and used them, the dolls broke easily. Little children are known for playing pretty roughly with their toys and the dainty mechanics were no match for their play. If the phonograph itself didn't break, the recordings wore out quickly. One sarcastic *Washington Post* headline blasted the invention saying, "Dolls That Talk: They Would Be More Entertaining if You Could Understand What They Say." People began angrily returning them to the stores.

"The voices of the little monsters were exceedingly unpleasant to hear."

—Thomas Edison

Back to the Drawing Board

In May 1890—yes, one month after they hit stores—the dolls were pulled from the shelves. Only around 2,500 were made, and fewer than 500 were sold. Many were stripped of their phonographs and resold as "regular" dolls... with vacant tin torsos. The Edison Talking Dolls were officially a failure. Edison himself was quoted as saying "the voices of the little monsters were exceedingly unpleasant to hear." He returned to the drawing board in order to create something better, but the company went into serious debt and shut down before Edison Talking Doll 2.0 emerged.

Few remain in the world today. Some of the recordings have been restored and, honestly, hearing a scratchy version of "Now I Lay Me Down to Sleep" is nightmare fodder. Please don't take our souls, Edison Talking Dolls.

Inspiration for Chucky? Edison's Talking Doll and a woman recording its voice.

#20 THE SUBMARINE TUBE

A TOTALLY TUBULAR ADVENTURE

1911–1916 | Virginia, United States & Nassau, Bahamas

Diving for treasure? Just pop into the water through the watertight tube, peer out of the portholes, put your arm through the hole-thingies, and grab that gold! Or not.

#20 The Submarine Tube

On Friday, May 12, 1911, the Ward liner *Merida* sank off the coast of Virginia after colliding with another steamship. Instead of moving away from the oncoming boat, the *Admiral Farragut* "rammed" her instead. News reports on the collision pointed out that passengers arrived in the city of New York "in scant attire" because they'd lost their luggage. Scandalous! Along with the luggage, $30,000 in bills and $750,000 in silver bars were donated to the ocean. Or $500,000 worth. Or millions. The number changed often.

Captain Charles Williamson of the Williamson Submarine Corporation in Virginia read about the sunken treasure and wanted to be the one to extract it from the bottom of the sea. He became a man with a mission. He'd already invented a waterproof apparatus a few years prior, which was designed to allow people who needed to be underwater such as treasure divers and submarine maintenance workers to access the ocean without getting wet. He hoped his invention would lead the future of the industry.

The tube was made out of iron rings attached to iron hinges, surrounded by a waterproof material, making it flexible and collapsible and airtight. It was often described as accordion-like. It came in multiple sections that could be attached depending on the depth it needed to reach. The top of it was secured above water to a boat and the bottom attached to a work chamber large enough to hold several people and that included portholes so they could see what they were doing. A ladder was used in the tube to reach the base.

"Flexible arms" into which workers stuck their own were patented by Williamson so that the workers could use their hands to fix whatever was needed under the boat (or seize that sought-after treasure). The device even had mechanical arms with claw grabbers that the operators could use to grasp bigger items. Not to mention interior and exterior lighting. It sounds AMAZING.

A Blip in History Best Forgotten

Two months after he read about the boat's demise, Williamson secured the contract to seek out the treasure using his invention. He was excited to show it off publicly. He brought it to the harbor closest to the sink site and attached it to a barge. He gave demonstrations and convinced experts it would work. Unfortunately, they sat waiting for months for a "seagoing vessel" that could venture out further to where the *Merida* waited all lonely on the bottom of the ocean. Not sure who fell down on that task, but that seems like the easiest part!

Once everything was set to go, Williamson tried for three weeks to get to the sunken ship. Mother Nature had other plans and the weather was continuously bad. They had to give up. Williamson's device was quickly forgotten as other less cumbersome salvage restoration apparatuses were invented. But the ship was a top-notch evader. Everyone failed. The *Merida*'s treasure still hasn't been resurrected. Mostly because everyone and their mom has been suing each other for the rights to access.

What the submarine tube would have looked like retrieving Merida's treasure, had it worked out.

Out of Failure Swims Success

The nice part was that even though Williamson's dreams sank with the *Merida*, his sons John Earnest (or J. E.) and George realized that the submarine tube could be used for underwater photography and moving film—a completely new concept for the time period. In 1912, J. E. updated the container that attached to the tube to make it camera-friendly, calling it a "photosphere." It was now a 4-ton, 6 foot by 10 foot (1.8 m by 3 m) globe made out of steel with a viewing chamber from which a camera operator could film the sea seen clearly outside. After tests in Norfolk Harbor, they gained backers who sent them to the Bahamas.

In 1914, they were off to Nassau. The water was perfect, clear and blue, even down to 150 feet (45 m). They had a special barge built with a large hole through which the tube and photosphere could be lowered into the sea. Huge Jules Verne fans, the brothers named it after the French author. The expedition was a huge success: They took oodles of photos, ranging from fish to shark hunts to naked divers; scientists even discovered new species by looking at the photos.

Next the brothers set their sights on making a movie of Verne's 1870 adventure *Twenty Thousand Leagues Under the Sea*. In addition to filming all underwater scenes in the movie (released 1916), J. E. actually built the giant 30ft (9 m) squid that attacked the ship. The Williamson family had altered how people could interact with the ocean. Thank goodness for dad Charles' invention, even if it never changed the submarine salvage industry—sometimes weird and crazy ideas have profitable outcomes down the road. Now if someone could just get to that *Merida* treasure...

#21 THE HINDENBURG
THE BUBBLE
THAT BURST

1937 | Lakehurst, New Jersey

In the 1930s, airships were the future. But maybe making
a flying machine filled with millions of cubic feet of highly
flammable gas was not the smartest idea?

#21 The Hindenburg

Airships were the first passenger aircraft to cross the Atlantic and fly around the world. They were the biggest aircraft ever built and the pinnacle of luxury air travel. But the very public and very fiery conflagration that destroyed the hydrogen-powered LZ 129 *Hindenburg* airship in New Jersey in 1937, killing thirty-five, stopped the airship revolution in its tracks.

In 1900, three years before the Wright brothers flew at Kitty Hawk, North Carolina, Count Ferdinand Graf von Zeppelin was flying passengers around the skies above Lake Constance in Germany in his LZ-1 airship. It wasn't a total success. At 420 feet (130 m) long with only four Daimler-Benz engines it was unwieldy and difficult to control, and a bit on the wobbly side. But the idea was sound. The concept was workable and, importantly, nobody died. His next models improved on the first one until he got to the LZ4, which in 1908 went on a twelve-hour flight over Switzerland and Germany, catching the public's imagination. Then, while it was tethered at Echterdingen in southern Germany, the balloon was ripped from its moorings by a sudden storm and it burst into flames. The German public were devastated, and in an early example of crowdfunding, they came up with enough money—6 million marks (approx. $1.5 million)—in donations for von Zeppelin to rebuild and continue his program.

Out for the Count
Then came World War I. Von Zeppelin's airships became weapons of war, dropping bombs all over Europe. The Treaty of Versailles following the end of the conflict placed heavy restrictions on German manufacturing of weapons, and airships were added to the banned list. The count died in 1917 but his company survived, largely because of an agreement they'd made to produce a huge airship for the US military— the USS *Los Angeles*. That commission kept the company ticking during the ban.

When restrictions were finally lifted, three enormous airships were planned: *Graf Zeppelin*, *Graf Zeppelin II*, and the *Hindenburg*. *Graf Zeppelin* was an amazing success. It flew 1 million miles (1.6 million km), circumnavigated the globe in twelve days, and carried a total of 13,110 passengers in opulent leather and linen surroundings.

Before and after photos of the Hindenburg.

#21 The Hindenburg

By the time the *Hindenburg* was completed in 1936, the superiority of airships over ocean liners for long distance travel had all but been proven. The *Hindenburg* started life equally successfully. It flew from Germany to the United States in around sixty hours and back in around fifty, making ten trips in all. It carried mail, cargo, and seventy passengers in first-class luxury. The future was bright. And then, suddenly, the future was snuffed out.

The Spark Heard Around the World

On May 6, 1937, the *Hindenburg* burst into flames above an airfield in New Jersey: the deaths of thirteen passengers and twenty-two crew were partly balanced by the miraculous survival of sixty-two other people. The explanation at the time, supported over eighty years of investigation, was that a spark ignited leaking hydrogen. Various conspiracies suspected foul play since the ship was adorned with swastikas and Germany was under the Nazi yolk and preparing for war at the time. But evidence suggests that a simple electrical discharge between the outer cover and the inner metal frame was enough to cause the giant airship to vanish in a sixty-second fireball.

Here comes the main problem with Zeppelin's airships. However quick and luxurious they were, the inescapable fact is that a balloon filled with 7 million cubic feet (around 200,000 cubic meters) of highly flammable gas is an accident waiting to happen. Seems obvious, doesn't it? In fact, following all the previous accidents leading up to the *Hindenburg* disaster, it seems strange that no one brought it up. No one said, "Are you sure this is a good idea?"

Well, someone thought it was. The *Hindenburg* was designed to use helium. Helium is not flammable, so it is much safer. But while hydrogen is cheap and easy to produce, helium is hugely expensive and difficult to come by. At the time, the United States was the only country producing enough helium to fill an airship. And in 1925, they passed the Helium Act, a law that forbade anyone from selling helium to foreign countries, especially foreign countries that might use it for airships in wartime. You know, like Germany did? So they reengineered the *Hindenburg* to use hydrogen—and, boom!

#22 HIGHWAY HI-FI
GET INTO THE GROOVE... WHILE DRIVING

1956 | New York City, New York

What could go wrong with putting a record player in a car?
Skip ahead to find out.

#22 Highway Hi-Fi

Peter Goldmark, an inventive and determined employee at Columbia Broadcasting System (CBS), unleashed the in-car record player on the world in 1956. In those days cars only had AM radio. In that landscape, consumers were definitely ready for the next big thing.

Goldmark was the man behind 33⅓ rpm (revolutions per minute) vinyl records. He headed up CBS Laboratories and was full of ideas. In a time dominated by long-playing records (LPs—the 33⅓ rpm ones) and 45 rpm records (invented by the Radio Corporation of America) that only held one song per side, Goldmark wanted to make something as long-playing as an LP but similar in size to a 45 so that it could easily go in a car. What he and his team came up with was a thicker, 7-inch playing surface that ran at a speed of 16⅔ rpm, allowing the same amount of song time on a standard LP but at a size that was more of a car-fit, along with the device to play them on. Brilliant!

Goldmark tested out the first one in his own Thunderbird and was excited to share it with his boss, CEO William Paley... who wasn't so thrilled. Paley saw the value in keeping drivers hooked on AM radio because it brought in advertising revenue. Goldmark didn't like listening to the radio, mostly that new-fangled rock 'n' roll that was popping up everywhere, so he went around his boss to Chrysler directly and pitched it to them.

After a flawless test drive with an executive at the company, Chrysler was sold on the idea. They purchased 18,000 of them and named the device the Highway Hi-Fi. They offered them in a handful of their car lines from 1956 through 1959. The actual unit was fitted under the dashboard and used the car's speakers to project the sound. It had a shockproof casing (debatable) and came with storage for six of the unique records. This was probably because it came with six pre-selected records. It had a door that would flip down, revealing the tiny player. To help with shock absorption, the needle was counterweighted and spring-loaded and came in from the side in order to make contact with the record, unlike a regular record player, where the operator placed the needle on top of the record. Chrysler claimed that it was immune to any hazards of the road. It added an extra $200 (around $1,700 in today's economy) to a car's sale price.

Classical Mistakes

As previously mentioned, Goldmark had pretty tame taste in music. The catalog was made up of classical music, jazz, theatrical performances... and absolutely no "modern" music. Additional records in these genres were sold and delivered via snail mail through their Columbia Records division. The original press release offered this enticing music collaboration: "For driver and passengers who prefer the lively scores of Broadway musicals, Highway Hi-Fi provides the lilting and memorable tunes from the hit show, *Pajama Game*." They even thought of the kids riding in the car with their parents! "And if the children are restless on a long ride, Davey Crockett and Gene Autry are ready at hand to help keep them quiet." Hmm, that's actually for the sanity of the parents.

That was really as far as the invention went, though. They had high warranties and consumers were not particularly interested in the limited music selection. Obviously, though, the main issue with records is that they skip. Goldman and team had worked very hard to make a needle that would do its darndest to reduce this unfortunate side effect. But it was in a car! Plus, it had been tested in high-end cars but offered (and not tested) in everyday cars that didn't have the same shock absorbency.

Mrs. Doubtfire test drives the Highway Hi-Fi.

> ## "If the children are restless on a long ride, Davey Crockett and Gene Autry are ready at hand to help keep them quiet..."

—Highway Hi-Fi press release

Putting the technology into any moving vehicle meant it would be subjected to violent movements as the driver negotiated potholes, swerved around obstacles in the road, and navigated sharp corners or missed turns (while screaming at the kids to shut up so they can actually hear Davey Crockett). Without a GPS screaming at them to "Turn right. Not that right!" it was probably a bit easier to get back on track, but no matter, it was not an ideal playing surface. When all was said and done, the Highway Hi-Fi was a flop. Today, however, they are highly collectable. Finding one, for some car enthusiasts, is like locating the Holy Grail. At least someone is making money from them!

If at First You Don't Succeed...
Chrysler didn't give up on the idea, though. They went on to another concept in the early 1960s from RCA that used the 45 rpm records. The device held fourteen of the smaller records and would cycle through them one at a time. Once a record finished, it would rest on the bottom of the unit. After all of the songs were played, the user would reload them and listen again. Kind of a pain, but the music choice wasn't limited because any 45 would work. But it didn't perform very well, either. The general population would need to wait until the better functioning four-track players were introduced a bit later.

#23 BETAMAX
LOSING THE TECHNO BATTLE

1975 | Japan and the United States

Sometimes bad ideas are good ideas that just get a crucial element wrong. Sony's Betamax had a head start over its rival VHS in the battle of home video systems. So how did VHS win the format war?

Happy Days made its television debut in 1974. If you weren't sitting on your couch the night that it aired, you simply missed Fonzie and Richie's first conversation. That was true of any television show in or before 1974—if you weren't around while your show was on, you had no way of seeing it later unless it re-aired someday. That all changed in 1975, when Sony introduced its Betamax Video Cassette Recorder (VCR)—and the concept of time-shifting—to the world. The Video Home System (VHS) format wouldn't show up until a year later.

Betamax vs. VHS

But let's go back in time for a moment. In 1969, just a few months after humans set foot on the moon, Sony introduced the U-matic. It was a video cassette recorder aimed at the consumer market, but it cost too much for most people. However, Hollywood, news stations, and other industries and institutions thought the U-matic and its three-quarter-inch tapes were affordable and easier to use—even if the color reproduction wasn't the best. Sony didn't give up on the consumer market, however, and in 1975 it released its new and improved recorder, the Betamax VCR. It got its name from *beta*, the Japanese word to describe how signals were recorded onto the tape, as well as the fact that the tape path of the new loading system looked like the Greek letter beta. The Betamax tape was two-thirds the weight of the U-matic and much smaller in size. However, it also only held an hour of recording. Sony thought that was plenty since it was the length of most American TV shows. Seven months before they launched Betamax, Sony invited executives from JVC and Radio Corporation of America (RCA) to preview the machine—and to try to get them on board with the Betamax standard. They didn't much like Sony's attitude, and JVC decided to do its own thing instead. Two years later, JVC would launch the VHS.

And the Winner Is...

In the beginning, the VHS had lower picture quality, but it could record two hours and was a lot less expensive for consumers. The first Betamax, the SL-6300, cost $2,295 (which would be nearly $11,000 today), while the VHS system was $1,280 ($5,410 in inflation-adjusted dollars). Turns out that not only were American consumers cheap, but they were also more interested in recording movies like *The Blues Brothers* than episodes of *Happy Days*. People in the United States recorded feature films more than any other type of programming—something that wasn't possible with the sixty-minute Betamax tapes. By the time Betamax released two-hour tapes, VHS could record up to four hours—long enough for a football game.

JVC did one other brilliant thing that made VHS the dominant format for many companies that produced VCRs—it gave its technology away for free. Sony, on the other hand, made companies pay for licenses to use its Betamax technology. Guess which format more companies chose? When video rental stores began to take off in the early 1980s, they went with the format that more of their customers owned, which meant more sales of VHS recorders to watch what was mostly available, and so on and so on.

And yes, porn had a role to play, too. Producers of porn, which was one of the main genres available at first, reportedly weren't allowed by Sony to publish on the Betamax format. Through the end of the 1970s, X-rated cassettes accounted for half of all pre-recorded sales. By 1980, VHS had 60 percent of the American market. In 1988, Sony threw in the towel and started selling the VHS format as well. Surprisingly, the last

> ## "The Betamax will allow you to break the time barrier."

—Sony promotional material

Betamax system was sold in 2002, and Betamax tapes were still manufactured until 2016. (It's just like people who still only listen to vinyl records—some still insist that Betamax is the only way to watch.)

The Lasting Legacy

Even though Betamax was a blip in entertainment history, it did have one huge effect on the way we record shows and movies today: It went to court with the film industry over whether consumers should even be allowed to record movies on their VCRs. In Sony Corp. v. Universal City Studios in 1984, Sony won at the Supreme Court when five of the nine justices voted that VCRs were OK for private use. Despite Sony's court victory, VHS continued to rule the format wars and was the standard of choice for many years after Betamax was relegated to the sidelines. Of course, DVDs showed up in 1997, and the last company in the world to make VHS recorders stopped producing them in 2016—the same year Betamax tapes stopped being made. Now if you'll excuse us, we're going to stream some episodes of *The Office*...

Chapter 5
EMPEROR'S NEW CLOTHES

#24 TESLA'S OSCILLATOR

WHOLE LOTTA SHAKIN' GOIN' ON

1890s | New York City, New York

Exploding windows, falling plaster, panicking neighbors... if you had invented a machine you believed could start an earthquake, would you use it in your own building? Perhaps not...

#24 Tesla's Oscillator

Nikola Tesla, after whom Elon Musk's electric cars are named, was a famous and somewhat notorious Serbian-American inventor operating in the late nineteenth and early twentieth centuries. Known for his brilliant mind and being a workaholic, he is rumored to have once been in the running for the Nobel Prize in Physics. His notoriety, however, comes from his rivalry with American inventor Thomas Edison, and his penchant for theatrical and public demonstrations of his machines that appeared to pay little concern to the health and safety of not only himself but anyone else in the near vicinity.

Good Vibrations

In the 1890s, he developed what was essentially a giant vibrator. The machine, called a "mechanical oscillator," was capable of moving a heavy weight backward and forward a tiny distance at tremendous speed. This regular, controllable vibration would be useful, say, for making an accurate clock, but the application for a bigger, heavier version was initially unclear. He stated that it would be used for mining and prospecting metals, but he was a little vague on the details. Tesla secretly hypothesized that even a fairly small version of his machine—clamped to an important piece of steel framework of, say, a partially constructed building—could get the steel to vibrate in sympathy at one of its "resonant frequencies," the effect spreading wider through the structure until... Well, until the building collapsed.

Shake, Rattle, and Roll

Keen to test his oscillator, Tesla popped a small prototype version of the device in his pocket and went looking for a building under construction. He found one near Wall Street in south Manhattan. Clamping his gismo to a steel beam (let's hope he checked no one was in the building at the time...) he adjusted the range and frequency of the oscillations until the beam started to hum. According to Tesla, the structure began to sway and creak and terrified workers ran out and called the cops. (Ah, apparently no, he didn't check the building was empty at the time!)

Tesla unclamped his oscillator and slipped away, but decades later said he was confident that—given ten minutes more—he could have "laid the building in the street." And given an hour he could "drop the Brooklyn Bridge into the East River."

At the time he kept his earthquake machine idea under wraps and instead obtained a patent for an "electric generator," in 1894, which included a vibrating element that "under the influence of an applied force such as the elastic tension of steam or a gas under pressure, yields an oscillation of constant period." This is a version of his earthquake machine, by another name.

A smoldering Tesla contemplates his powers of destruction.

Quaking It?

In 1898 he reportedly tested an oscillator in his lab building in Houston Street, New York. The results were so successful that the neighbors contacted the emergency services reporting an earthquake. He found a resonant frequency for his own building, and the effect spread to neighboring buildings for many blocks around. Windows exploded, pipes for gas and water broke, plaster fell from ceilings. Heavy machinery in factories broke free and danced across the floor.

Tesla terminated the experiment pretty sharpish—by smashing the oscillator with a sledgehammer—when it became obvious that a catastrophe endangering the lives of thousands of people was just moments away. Or perhaps out of fear that the cops might discover his building was the source of the vibrations!

Some four decades later Tesla revealed that he was responsible for the earthquake of East Houston Street with a little device "you could put in your overcoat pocket." He said: "The building would have been about our ears in another few minutes. Outside in the street there was pandemonium. The police and ambulances arrived. I told my assistants to say nothing. We told the police it must have been an earthquake. That's all they ever knew about it."

Tesla's original prediction—that his oscillator could be used to locate oil and minerals—came true. Using vibrations like radar, deposits of oil and minerals deep beneath the Earth's surface can be ascertained, and oil companies have benefited hugely from this discovery.

The Truth Hertz

Was it an earthquake machine? Well, Tesla did state that using the principals of his oscillator, you could "split the Earth in half like an apple," but such claims remain unproved. As he pointed out himself, there is a reason soldiers break step when they cross a bridge. Resonant frequencies can be devastating. But while it is possibly true that he could drop the Brooklyn Bridge with a pocket oscillator, the resonant frequency of a steel structure is a lot easier to find than that of a mass of loose and different, unattached materials. Which is, you know, just as well.

#25 ELECTRIFIED WATER
RECHARGE YOUR BATTERIES

Early 1900s | United States

These days, energy drinks (full of ingredients that are possibly not from the Earth) are hailed as good for your energy levels. But the idea isn't new. Enter electrified water…

#25 Electrified Water

Electricity was a hot commodity for city dwellers back in the early twentieth century. Homes were getting lit. Candles were feeling neglected. The air was alive with power. In addition to the basic ways in which electricity improved the quality of life for the average person, charlatans were out in droves trying to make a quick buck off of people's ignorance. All sorts of face-palm situations occurred.

Putting the "Buzz" in "Buzzword"

For a time, "electrified water" was all the rage. The concept behind this oxymoronic sounding process was that if a charge was added to still water, it would enhance it with life-altering elements. These would then transfer to the person drinking or using it. Plants would grow larger and faster. Clothes would be cleaner. Hangovers would be cured!

Before your head fills up with the image of a person sipping from a glass that's plugged into the wall, hair shooting out electrocution-style, the water didn't have a current passing actively through it while in contact with a human. Bummer, I know. It would be a heck of a lot more entertaining if people were running around electrocuting themselves.

One hope was that the electrification would cure horrible waterborne diseases still plaguing people, like cholera and typhoid. But people also wanted to make their lives easier and better. Quality of life still had a long way to go. This novel concept was probably as good as any others out there to try.

Step Right Up!

Most of the info about the process and offerings have survived in ads buried in the annals of the Internet. The Imperial Laundry Co. in New Mexico placed an ad in the *Albuquerque Morning Journal* in March 1913 boasting about its new "absolute sterilization" "electric process." They no longer used "Chloride of Lime" when cleaning clothes. Over and over they emphasized that "We Now Positively Guarantee Complete" sterilization, deodorization, prevention of color running, and longer-lasting linen. They even invited consumers to visit the business to watch the entire process live. And they also placed emphasis on not having "dark corners" in their business. This claim definitely produces an image of workers in a secret back room furiously scrubbing clothing with soap.

In the *Daily Ardmoreite* in December 1918, the Electrified Water Company of Texas put out an ad stating they had a "fine opportunity for a live business man" to own his own water bottle business. They claimed their sterilizer provided "pure, clean, sweet-tasting water." Maybe they specified "live" because after coming in contact with the water, he became a zombie?

In a tiny square of a page in *The Washington Times* in October 1922, a woman is shown dipping her hands into a large bowl of water. Electrical cords are shown in the water with her. It claims "FOR THE MORNING AFTER, placing the hands in a bowl of electrified water is said by physicians to be a sure cure for headaches. The water is electrified by means of a simple apparatus." Um. She was actually touching a live current. Who are these physicians? Why is there no further information??

In the end, electrified water didn't really cure anything. SHOCKING. Or not shocking? Whomp whomp. Amped-up water had fizzled out.

Don't look now—you might get a nasty shock.

Other Hairbrained Ideas

Instead of boosting water with electrical currents, some scientists tried using radiation. *Radiation*. Added to water. Which people drank. Bottles were infused with low levels of radium or a radium-soaked device was placed in the bottle. And then, you know, it was ingested.

Back on electricity, why boost water when it was much easier to shock the person directly? Among myriad gadgets and doodads that promised incredible results were electric belts. Many looked like chastity belts and fired electric pulses directly at the body—and cured just about everything (according to anyone who invented one). One former politician—a professional liar, if you will—named his product the I-On-A-Co. He said his "life belt" had cured him by increasing the oxygen absorbed by the body and freed it of all "toxic diseases."

What about Dr. Scott's Electric FLESH Brush? It promised to cure "headache and neuralgia in five to seven minutes." Not sure how much flesh got brushed with it... He also offered an electric toothbrush ("A Remarkable Invention") and, wait for it, an electric CORSET ("ABSOLUTELY UNBREAKABLE"). Dr. Scott sure was busy! Along with the rest of the charlatans. Quack, quack!

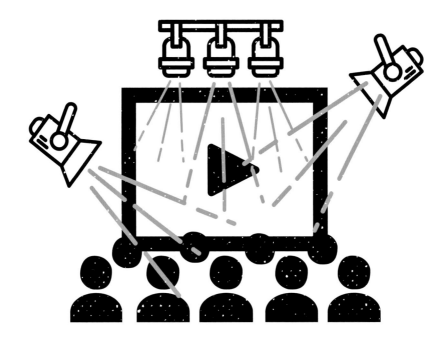

#26 DAYLIGHT CINEMA
MOVIES WITH THE LIGHTS ON?

c.1910 | Forest City, Pennsylvania

Samuel "Roxy" Rothapfel, the man who brought us the Rockettes and Radio City Music Hall, also came up with a literal bright idea—daylight cinema—that turned out to be a flash in the pan.

#26 Daylight Cinema

There are many reasons people go to the movie theater—to see a good film, to sit in the air conditioning for a couple hours, or to have fun in a dark room with a date. Samuel "Roxy" Rothapfel was clearly a fan of making movies fun, but his daylight motion picture system put a stop to clandestine hand-holding and secret kisses in the dark for a few years, starting in 1910. He claimed you could see the picture just as well as in the dark, if not better—but this crucial point is where his idea ran aground.

First Act

Roxy opened his Family Theater in the back room of a saloon where he bartended in Forest City. He lived by the motto, "Don't give the people what they want—give them something better." So instead of just showing silent films in the theater, he added a skating rink for kids. He hired the most talented musicians he could find to play during the silent films. He did things like putting rose petals in front of fans to spread the perfume during a movie with the Tournament of Roses. And yes, he started projecting films in a fully lit theater to help patrons "avoid eye fatigue," among other reasons.

In an advertisement in the local paper in 1910, Roxy bragged: "I offer for your approval the absolutely flickerless picture and guarantee that they will not even tire the most sensitive eyes." Before then, many patrons apparently felt "agitation and objection to" motion picture houses because "audiences have been obliged to sit in absolute darkness." Women and young girls would be much safer if they could see who was in the theater with them—after all, who knew what naughty things could happen in the dark?

In all honesty, his idea for lighted theaters probably derived more from the need to seem "respectable" so that everyone in the town would visit his theater, especially the middle-class women and their children, whose pennies would be critical to the movie theater's success. Roxy not only managed to prevent attacks from moral crusaders, but the lighted movie theaters were seen as an excellent alternative to the saloons by temperance movement activists.

Second Act

Word of his over-the-top shows spread, and Roxy was offered a column in the trade publication *Moving Picture World*. A hustler who knew how to sell himself, he ensured his reputation grew with every column, and soon theaters all over the country wanted to hire him. The Lyric Theater in Minneapolis, for example, needed someone to bring the patrons through its struggling doors. Roxy took over, and when it reopened in 1911, its lights were kept on during the films. (He also added an electric fountain and a children's playground.)

The idea of daylight motion pictures spread across the country. Apparently unchaperoned teen girls were a big concern, raising fears of sexual promiscuity. A *Chicago Tribune* reporter, for example, was concerned that the girls he saw would make undesirable acquaintances of men of "mature age," and who knew what chaos would ensue? A bill in California required theaters to use Roxy's technology so theatergoers could always see other attendees. It was clearly meant to tamp down on immoral behavior, as the bill also included a curfew for minors and prohibited plays that depicted crimes. The bill, of course, only spread the word about his system. In 1911, even Madison Square Garden Theater, with its 5,000 seats, had a daylight screen installed.

Roxy was a master of marketing and advertising, drumming up fears of impropriety and eye strain in publications so theaters would clamor for his invention. Conveniently, only Roxy knew the secret of how to make daylight cinema. This meant that only he could sell and profit from the installation of his system—not so dumb!

Final Act

As projectionists across the country became more skilled, however, many of them had negative comments about the system. The same trade publication that Roxy had written for said that daylight pictures "lacked sharpness and intensity," and

Artist's impression of a fully lit theater, rendering the moving picture much sharper than it was in reality.

others pointed out that there was actually little that was "secret" about how he did it. It seemed to be hardly more than smoke and mirrors, and a whole lot of clever marketing. Eventually, theaters would go back to dark auditoriums, and Roxy soon moved on to bigger and better hustles.

Once he made it to NYC in 1912, he opened the Roxy Theater at Times Square, Radio City Music Hall, and the RKO Roxy. The Roxy featured a dance troupe named after him, called the Roxyettes. They would later become the famed Rockettes at the Radio City Music Hall, where they have continued to perform an over-the-top spectacle on a lighted stage for more than 75 million audience members since 1933. Movies with the lights on? Who needs them?

#27 THE PET ROCK

PET THAT ROCKS THE NATION

1975 | Los Gatos, California

Does your landlord say "No!" to pets? Are you tired of the daily hassle of caring for an animal that your child promised to care for? So... why not buy a pet rock instead?!

It was 1975 and down-on-his-luck freelance advertising copywriter Gary Dahl was at a bar in California with his buddies. His friends were all moaning into their drinks, fed up with taking care of the pets in their respective homes. Poking a bit of fun at the group, he told them that he already had the perfect pet. It took very little maintenance; it didn't even have to be cleaned up after! He was talking about his pet rock—a creation he'd made up on the spot. Instead of finishing his beer and leaving the concept at the bar, he realized there might be something in the idea.

Since words were his bread and butter, he started by writing a training manual for these tiny, low-stress "genuine, pedigreed" creatures. "They descend from a long line of famous rocks." The book outlined all the reasons why rocks were better pets than animals. And it was packed with tricks any rock worth its weight should have been able to master. There was even a special section on Attack Training, should someone try to injure the owner. Obviously, it was instructions on how to throw the Pet Rock at the attacker.

Excerpts from *The Care and Training of Your Pet Rock*:

"Nobody, but nobody, likes a surly, misbehaving rock."

"The best place to teach your Pet Rock to Roll Over is on a hill."

Once the manual was complete, he found a couple of investors and went in search of the perfect rock. He settled on the Rosarito Beach Stone from Mexico, a smooth rock that was also super cheap. Each cost only a penny. He decided to package every Pet Rock in its own cardboard pet carrier, complete with holes and all. A rock needs to breathe! Each one was carefully placed on a bed of wood shavings. And, in quite the sneaky move, he added the printing of the thirty plus-page manual (complete with illustrations) on to one of his clients' jobs without their knowledge. All in all, the cost of each one was miniscule compared to what it would make in sales. In line with his playful nature and his circumstances before the invention, he named his company Rock Bottom Productions.

Rolling out the Pet Rock

It was nearing Christmas 1975 when he rocketed off to the San Francisco Gift Show—a less competitive environment than the world's toy fairs—with the completed kit, ready to sell the world on his unique idea. Neiman Marcus saw the novelty in it and snapped up an order of 500 right off the bat. Other companies quickly followed suit. Once the Pet Rocks hit shelves, they flew right back off of them. They were "The hit of the year!" according to many media sources. They were priced at $3.95, and Dahl netted around $1 off of each one sold, making him wealthy beyond his wildest dreams almost instantly.

For a few months, sales continued to soar. The product was so popular that Dahl appeared on *The Tonight Show* and newspapers ran all sorts of articles on him and his invention. But the fad faded fast and six months after it had swept the nation, purchases plummeted. With no way to trademark the idea, copycats popped up. People—Dahl called them "wackos"—hounded him with their own hairbrained ideas, hoping they, too, would make a fortune. And the original backers sued him because they felt like they should have made more money by investing. They won, taking a slice of his profits. The time had come to bury the Pet Rock. Dahl shed few tears, though. With the $1 profit on each one and the sale of around 1.5 million pets, he went from struggling writer to millionaire.

He continued trying to think up one-hit wonders. Take the "Sand Breeding Kit" from 1976, for example. Packaged in another cardboard box, this "field-tested" kit came with a tube of "genuine breeding," "male" sand and another tube of "female" sand that were intended to mate. It also came with a funny guide, instructing the owner on how to breed them. But the public wasn't taking the bait this time and it failed hard. In 2001, decades after his fluke success, he wrote *Advertising for Dummies*. The irony of that title combo should not be lost. Genius or lucky swindler or both, Dahl was no dummy.

Even Dahl seems surprised to find a rock packaged up ready to hit the shelves.

#28 HAIR IN A CAN
SHINY DOME TO... PLUSH RUG

1980s and 1990s | United States

Presenting: spray-on hair. Airbrush those bald patches
with a quick squirt of a can. What could possibly go wrong?
Well, the jury's still (a long way) out on this one...

#28 Hair in a Can

In 1982, American entrepreneur Mark Kress saw the problem of thinning hair and looked for a cosmetic solution for men and women that would be better than previous attempts (such as mascara and toupees). He created Toppik powdered hair using wool because it was similar (sure...) to human hair due to the keratin in both substances. The wool was powdered and colored to build texture and volume rather than being a one-dimensional spray color that was as good as boot polish and it was designed to be sprinkled onto hair. Without the funding to take the product further, however, he set it aside for some time until after the success of another, similar product: GLH.

In the early 1990s, inventor, fast-talker, and successful salesman Ron Popeil was in his stride. He'd invented the Smokeless Ashtray, the Inside-the-Egg Scrambler... the list goes on. But was the world ready for his next, inspired product? Oh, yes. GLH-9 (Great Looking Hair Formula #9, of course) was about to revolutionize the lives of balding men and women with thinning hair across the United States. In fact, Popeil didn't invent the spray-on rug, he bought the rights to the idea from two separate Australian inventors and, along with product designer Alan Backus, experimented with both formulas to make it look more realistic.

There are two main types of hair in a can. One works by adding color to the scalp and thickening any hair that's left in the area; the other type creates powdery "hair" fibers that stick to the scalp and to any remaining real hairs, giving an illusion of density. GLH-9 was the second, fibrous type. A "cosmetic styling aid" liquid spray that dried as a powder, it was marketed by Popeil's company, Ronco.

They sold nearly 1 million units in a year at the princely sum of $39.92 each, or $110 for a month's supply including three cans: One hair thickener, one finishing shield, one hair cleanser to wash it out. Eternal youth comes at a high price. A similar package was billed at $135, including an instructional video, but, in typical infomercial shopping fashion, was sold for a special price of $19.95 if "bought now."

Emperor's New Clothes

When Ronco first brought out GLH it was available in seven different hair hues. But you were overlooked if you were a redhead, as Popeil didn't deem these handsome types a large enough part of the population to be viable. Popeil had founded Ronco in 1964, to market mainly kitchen gadgets via infomercials. His slick, persuasive style of selling was to be adopted by most shopping channels for decades to come and helped Ronco market its products very successfully in some cases. And hair loss is a big (and justifiably sensitive) market to target, with 85 percent of men losing hair by age fifty, and the numbers climb with age, not forgetting women affected by hair loss.

Hair Today...

In the 1990s, before we had the bells and whistles of HDTV, the demos that Popeil carried out in his infomercials looked pretty convincing. Not so much in real life, though. He made an extended infomercial with an audience of hair-loss sufferers and brought up unsuspecting audience members to spray their patchy pates to seemingly amazing effect. Popeil claimed GLH made people look years younger and gave them renewed confidence. The audience were wowed and vowed to buy the product. Subsequent reviews of the various types of spray-on hair on the market are not so amazing, though, and the jury is out as to whether it does actually work, with most describing it as a messy, powdery waste of time. And every now and then photos circulate on social media of the latest celebrity to try out hair in a can and end up looking like G. I. Joe's been playing with boot polish. On his head.

Today, we have the choice of many brands of powdery, canned hair, piggy-backing on the success of GLH and playing on the sensitivity of the hair-loss market. Hair in a can isn't sprayed these days, it's more usually sprinkled, like Kress's invention, and is a fibrous powder of electrostatically charged keratin fibers for thickening hair temporarily. The spray-on version (essentially spray paint, let's be honest) did not have the longevity of the sprinkled powder version, and Ronco went bankrupt in 2007, but the instant success of GLH means hair in a can will forever be thought of and known as spray-on hair, even if it isn't, you know, sprayed on. Just remember to stay out of the rain, folks.

Hair in a can: For those thinning on top it puts hairs on the chest... legs and arms.

Chapter 6
CAN OF WORMS

#29 ASBESTOS TABLEWARE
THE SHAH'S UNBURNABLE NAPKIN

590 CE | Iran

The adverse effects of asbestos on the lungs were known as early as the time of the Ancient Greeks and Romans, so using it for tablecloths and napkins might not have been such a smart idea...

#29 Asbestos Tableware

Khosrow II—the last long-term king, or shah, of the Sasanian dynasty—ascended the Iranian throne in 590 CE and set about conquering Roman provinces. He was a particularly affluent king, with many, many treasures, including solid gold furniture decorated with rubies, and an exotic menagerie. But what was the one thing a wealthy Sasanian king didn't have? Why, an asbestos napkin, of course.

Killer Cloth

Asbestos is a group of at least six similar silicate minerals with sharp, heat-resistant fibers which form a flossy texture when processed. It is familiar to many today as building insulation but it had been known about since the Neolithic era, when people used it to temper ceramics. It seemed like a wonder material and was named asbestos ("inextinguishable") by the Ancient Greeks. We know that in this era people valued its heat- and fire-resistant qualities. But they also noticed its adverse effects on the lungs. Inhalation of the fibers or their invisible, microscopic dust causes various forms of cancer to manifest decades later, as well as lung diseases. Useful, but deadly.

Unfortunately, though, the material's heat resistance made it a winner at Khosrow's court. How about a napkin that doesn't need to be cleaned with water? In fact, you don't even need to shake off the crumbs—instead, it can be thrown onto the fire, for an intensive, deep clean in mere seconds. Set aside the deadly effects of the napkin, which might come decades later... Though that wasn't something Khosrow would have to worry about, given he would be prematurely executed by his son.

You could say that Khosrow was ahead of his time with his own version of "dry" cleaning. What's more, asbestos gave him the opportunity to shine at his fancy dinners, when he wowed unsuspecting guests with his party trick of dabbing his mouth then throwing the pestilent cloth into the fire. Ooh! Aah! It doesn't burn, and it comes out whiter than white! Pity the poor workers who made the fabric, though, as they would have been exposed to large amounts of the deadly dust during production.

While Khosrow probably didn't invent the asbestos napkin, he was one of the first to be recorded as having owned one. And he wasn't the only one to see the value in the heat-resistant properties of this "wonder" fabric. In the eighth century, France's King Charlemagne requested tablecloths made with asbestos, in order to counter the regular fire hazard of candles getting knocked over at boozy banquets. He also reportedly performed that party trick of throwing it on the fire to clean it after eating, much to guests' amazement.

Long History of Ignorance

Despite the Romans and Greeks noticing the effect asbestos had on the lungs of workers who came into contact with it, the dangers of the material were largely ignored over the centuries. The modern asbestos mining industry began during the Industrial Revolution. Risks were hinted at in the late nineteenth century when certain doctors warned of its fatal effects. But it wasn't until the 1970s that the effects of the lethal mineral were finally taken seriously and it began to be phased out—too late for the poor souls who had already been exposed during their working lives.

The widespread use of asbestos as insulation in public buildings means the risks continue even to this day. There are now regulations in place in many countries, and asbestos is banned in some. These regulations have helped to contain the general public's exposure to asbestos. At least we don't have to worry about asbestos tablecloths and napkins, however. Small mercies.

Asbestos was everywhere.

The Wonderful Uses of Asbestos

In the 1930s and 1940s, asbestos fabric was widely used, from head-to-toe firefighter suits and other "safety"(!) clothing, to fireproof tablecloths, curtains, and chair covers in the home. "They are one answer to the problem of the careless smoker. Ash, but no char!" said a 1942 British Pathé short film promoting "The Wonderful Uses of Asbestos" to housewives of the time.

Someone even had the bright idea of using asbestos in books. Just in case you want to read in, you know, a volcano. Or something. Thankfully, this use was restricted and not on general sale, with the exception of a few first editions, including Ray Bradbury's *Fahrenheit 451*, which was inscribed with the words "This edition of FAHRENHEIT 451 has been limited to 200 copies. It is specially bound in JOHNS-MANVILLE QUINTERRA, an asbestos material with exceptional resistance pyrolysis."

#30 NOBEL'S DYNAMITE

IT'LL BLOW YOUR SOCKS OFF

1866 | Stockholm, Sweden

Alfred Nobel developed dynamite for mining. But others found violent and deadly uses for his explosive invention. A good idea gone bad.

Mining has existed since ancient times. The list of extracted substances is exhaustive, including salt, oil, coal, copper, gold, and diamonds (in the case of Snow White and the Seven Dwarfs). Well, there were others who also mined diamonds... It wasn't until the ninth century when black powder was invented in China that explosives were used in the process.

Skipping forward to the 1800s, when black powder was still the main substance used in controlled mining explosions, scientists wanted to develop better alternatives. Nitroglycerin, a volatile explosive, was created in 1846 by Italian chemist Ascanio Sobrero, who added nitric and sulfuric acid to glycerol. The substance was used to blast rocks and create tunnels, but it was incredibly unstable and unpredictable.

Alfred Nobel was an engineer. He'd constructed numerous buildings and bridges in his home city of Stockholm and wanted a better process for removing the pesky rocks blocking his way. He started by inventing and patenting a detonating blast cap in 1863 for use with the nitroglycerin. It created a powerful shock that heated the explosive instead of the traditional technique that relied on heat combustion.

The Real Big Bang

During his years of experimentation, deaths occurred. Nobel's younger brother Emil was killed in 1864 in a factory explosion along with a handful of workers. Saddened, Nobel wanted to make the nitroglycerin safer. The blast cap was clearly not enough. His next step was the creation of a substance called "blasting oil" that mixed nitroglycerin with black powder. Unfortunately, fifteen people died in a factory when the new substance exploded in a closet. Far from safer.

Still frustrated, Nobel focused on improving Sobrero's recipe in 1866. By adding a silica absorbing agent to the mixture, he was able to make a moldable explosive paste, which he patented as dynamite. (Actually, he first called it Nobel's Blasting Powder, but that was a mouthful, so he renamed it.) Dynamite could be shaped into cylinders and then shoved into drilled holes in the rocks. The result was much more dependable. Still feeling that it was a bit unsafe, he added a fuse, which helped enormously. This prevented miners from having to light the explosives and run away screaming as they went off. (Speculation, of course.)

It's Not All Fun and Games

The horrific uses of dynamite by the military wreaked havoc in new ways. Here are just two examples of the misery the invention caused. During the Spanish-American War in 1898, it was used in cannons, a truly brutal delivery system. Then in 1916, an artificial island in the New York Harbor, called Black Tom, was turned into a huge ammunition hub. About 75 percent of all weapons used in World War I were shipped from there. The United States was still neutral and sold to both sides, but the Allied countries bought most of them. Germany wasn't too happy about that and plotted to blow up the island using dynamite.

On July 30, the explosion caused a catastrophic chain reaction and included the detonation of eighty-seven dynamite-filled railroad cars. The island was basically destroyed, and the mainland was also affected. Around $20 million worth of damage was inflicted, and many lives were lost. Officials weren't convinced that Germany was behind it, instead accusing the island's workers of neglect. Litigation went on for decades, with Germany finally losing. Kind of like the war.

Back in 1888 when Nobel's other brother Ludvig passed, journalists mistakenly thought it was the better-known sibling. The obituaries written about Alfred Nobel were not kind. He was called, among other things, "the merchant of death." And he was accused of making tons of money off "finding ways to kill more people faster than ever before." Reading his obituaries (while still alive!) devastated him—Alfred Nobel was a pacifist!

Peace Out

Not wanting to be remembered so negatively, he decided to create the Nobel Prize. In his last will and testament in 1895, a year before he died, he pledged the majority of his wealth be awarded to five recipients each year. The prizes would be for those "who, during the preceding year, have conferred the greatest benefit to humankind." No one saw the will until after his death, and it caused quite a stir with family members who were expecting big bucks. The will was finally honored, and the first official prize was awarded in 1901. The five Nobel Prize categories are for physics, chemistry, literature, medicine, and, closest to Nobel's heart, peace. How's that for going out with a bang?

Alfred Nobel ponders how it all got so explosively out of hand.

#31 HYDROGENATED OILS
THE TRANS FAT TRAVESTY

1897–1911 | Europe and the United States

Hydrogenated oils began by keeping people clean—in soap form.
It seemed a neat idea to add them to foodstuffs, but then their
negative effects on health became clear… So, not so smart.

#31 Hydrogenated Oils

Animal fats were scarce in the late nineteenth century, so vegetable oils, solidified to make soap in a new process called hydrogenation, came to the rescue for grubby people across the land. This was all well and good until people started to eat them and that's when the problems began.

Not the soap. Nineteenth-century folk weren't so backward that they ate soap! Hydrogenation—adding hydrogen to plant oils—revolutionized not just the soap industry but also the food industry, by allowing vegetable fats to compete with animal fats in solid form. Margarine and shortening could stand in for butter and lard. This was important because it both increased the shelf life and brought the cost down. But the impact on health from eating hydrogenated fats wasn't apparent until further down the line.

Not only does hydrogenation change a liquid oil into a solid fat, it can also improve the taste of the oil, particularly if it's used more than once for frying or kept for a long time. It does this by stopping oxygen from getting in and turning the oil rancid—the hydrogen acts as a firewall, blocking that oxygen from entering. On the other hand, it does make certain oils taste blander, so it's not necessarily always a good thing in this respect. And did we mention the health implications? Partially hydrogenated oils contain trans fats, which increase the bad cholesterol (low density lipoprotein or LDL) and actually reduce the good cholesterol (high density lipoprotein or HDL) in the body. Not a good combination.

Ironically, like animal fats, fully hydrogenated oil doesn't have much trans fat in it and is far healthier, but partially hydrogenated fats are what was put into many foodstuffs because they are cheaper and therefore save producers money plus which they give products a longer life. It's just a shame about the shorter life they bring to consumers given the increased risk of heart attack or stroke, not to mention long-term conditions such as diabetes.

Come on children, eat up your trans fats. Advertisement for an Oleomargarine product, 1919.

Fat Lot of Good That Invention Did

Solid animal fats such as lard and butter were becoming scarce due to high demand and therefore very expensive around the turn of the twentieth century. Being able to use plant oils in their place was a pipe dream until, in France in 1897, chemists Paul Sabatier and Jean-Baptiste Senderens came along. They made the ground-breaking discovery that vegetable oils are not as solid as their animal-fat counterparts because they have less hydrogen in them. The dream was to use vegetable oils in the soap-making process. They developed a way of hydrogenating vapors using a catalyst (nickel) around 1901, and Sabatier later went on to win the Nobel Prize in chemistry for his work with catalysts (1912).

However, there were flaws in their plan, and German scientist Wilhelm Normann pointed them out (with some satisfaction, it seems). He built on the work of Sabatier and Senderens to finally, in 1902, accomplish that golden dream of turning liquid oil into solid fat, or "trans fat," and patented the process. In order to make the process commercially viable for soap, Normann worked with several companies including

#31 Hydrogenated Oils

Joseph Crosfield & Sons of Warrington, England. Around the same time, a German factory began using a similar process to make vegetable margarine (Tomor) for Jewish consumers, who had strict dietary requirements of keeping meat and dairy separate.

The turning point came in 1911 in the United States, when Procter & Gamble bought Normann's patent and marketed a hydrogenated food product from cottonseed oil: Crisco vegetable shortening. This marked the start of mass-market, plant-based margarines and shortenings becoming available from a number of companies, followed by partially hydrogenated fat being added to all kinds of processed foods. With a side of heart attack, perhaps.

Chewing the Fat
Consumption of margarine and other products containing partially hydrogenated fats increased during World War II, when animal products were hard to find. Then, in the 1980s, saturated fats (from animals) were outed as being a cause of heart disease, so plant-based fats began to be consumed in larger numbers instead. Bring on the 1990s, and evidence of the dangers of trans fats was uncovered, so the balance swung once again. Confused?

Tomor and Crisco are still available today, but with negligible or no amounts of partially hydrogenated fats in them. Due to consumer demand and regulations in various countries since the 2000s, most margarines now have no trans fats in them, and palm oil (semi-solid at room temperature) is often used instead. (Which brings with it other problems—for the environment—but that's another story. And perhaps it's balanced out by not eating butter, which may have a higher carbon footprint thanks to the methane produced by the animal industry.) There are two sides to every story, and some scientists are in disagreement as to the true risks of hydrogenated oils via trans fats and whether animal fats are better for us or not. What is known for sure is that a diet high in any fat is bad. Low fat = good. Everything in moderation, as they say.

#32 CFCS

BLOWING THE ROOF OFF THE PLANET

1930s | Dayton, Ohio

One scientist delivered two deadly blows to the atmosphere. His invention of ozone-destroying CFCs was preceded by his development of leaded gasoline. Worst inventor ever?

#32 CFCs

In the 1930s Thomas Midgely Jr. was hired by the Frigidaire division of General Motors to find a non-toxic, non-flammable alternative to the currently highly dangerous chemicals used in refrigeration units and air conditioners. The search for a stable chemical that wouldn't release any noxious gases led Midgley's team to develop Freon. It was the world's first chlorofluorocarbon (CFC).

CFCs were highly volatile (which in chemical terms mean they quickly turned into a gas). They were very useful for all kinds of refrigeration, and also as a propellant for things like aerosol spray cans. Midgley and his team were celebrated and he was given all sorts of awards. Now, of course, the effect of CFCs on the atmosphere is widely understood. Once released, CFCs zip into the high atmosphere surrounding the Earth and release halogen atoms that cause ozone destruction. This special layer of the atmosphere protects the earth from the sun's UVB rays. Less ozone means more UVB rays, which means more sunburn, skin cancer, and cataracts. In 1987, the Montreal Protocol banned the production of CFCs. Happily, this has led to ozone levels stabilizing. Recovery is predicted to continue until, around 2075, we will be back to the ozone level we had before.

Curiously CFCs were not the only terrible thing Thomas Midgely Jr. inflicted on the world. His smart-looking inventions have turned out the dumbest of the dumb because of the havoc they have wreaked.

Spitball... and Lead in Gasoline

At quite an early age, Midgely had already cemented his name as a thoroughly antisocial character. In high school, he discovered that the chewed bark of the slippery elm tree could be used to cheat at baseball by making the ball fly funny. His spitball infected all of baseball. Not content with just ruining the United States' favorite game, he moved on to the United States' favorite pastime. In 1916, Midgely joined the Kettering auto parts company. Cars at the time were taking off in a big way. He was responsible for trying to make a smoother running engine. The problem, called "knock," was uneven fuel burning, and it made engines shaky, noisy, and unreliable. Midgley tried adding every chemical known to man to gasoline to solve the problem. Then he found a winner. Lead.

Lead Me Tell You a Story

The toxic substance has long been known as poisonous, even as far back as the early Roman Empire. Pliny the Elder had some insight into its perils in the first century. He noticed that drinking wine sweetened with lead caused "paralytic hands." (Yes, back then they added lead to wine. And then drank it. Despite understanding at the time that consuming lead could cause health problems, madness, and even death.) The toxic substance would continue to be used in makeup, paint, coins, cups, and plates, and as a condiment for centuries. Possibly the biggest indicator that it was a terror was that it was known to be used as a poison to kill off relatives who were in the way. The French called it *"poudre de la succession"*—"succession powder."

It worked like a dream. A 0.25 addition to 100 parts of gasoline cured the knock. It was revolutionary. Engines purred all over the country. But then people started getting sick and dying. Sixty workers at the Dayton fuel works contracted lead poisoning, and two of them died. Even Midgely himself had to take six weeks off work to recover from sickness.

Life is Cheap. Our Gas? Not So Much.

It shouldn't have come as a surprise. The deadly qualities of lead were widely known before they started adding it to fuel. But it was very cheap, worked great, and the extra price charged for a gallon of magic no-knock fuel returned a huge profit. Lead fuel additives would eventually be banned in the 1970s, except for aviation fuel. The amount of damage to public health caused by adding lead to gasoline—the impairment to children's developing brains and the number of deaths—is impossible to quantify but is likely to be terrifyingly huge.

#32 CFCs

Through ignorance largely but negligence certainly, Thomas Midgley Jr. might be the human who singularly has caused the most harm in the entire history of mankind. He might take top place on the podium ahead of despots and tyrants who have slaughtered millions. The full extent of the damage he has caused and the lives he has cost may not be realized for decades to come, if ever...

Harmful Freon-containing aerosol, shooting CFCs into the atmosphere.

#33 DDT

MOSQUITO KILLER MISFIRES

1939 | Switzerland

DDT seemed like the miracle needed to stop the spread of malaria and typhoid. But we're still dealing with its environmental effects today—and the fact that we don't have anything nearly as effective to replace it.

#33 DDT

Swiss chemist Paul Mueller was looking for an insecticide that was long-lasting and cheap to produce when he stumbled on dichlorodiphenyltrichloroethane (DDT) during his research in 1939. It would save the lives of millions during World War II and go on to be used extensively in agriculture. But people soon started asking questions about its effects on the balance of nature and on humans. Environmental scientist Rachel Carson's 1962 *Silent Spring* was instrumental in sparking concern about the environment in general and DDT specifically, leading to the pesticide's ban in 1972 in the United States.

The Magic Bullet
DDT was actually first created in 1874 by a Viennese man who never really investigated its properties. Mueller discovered its effectiveness as a pesticide when he was looking for something to control pests after a major food shortage in Switzerland was caused by crop infestations and a lethal typhus epidemic in Russia was spread by insects. Mueller went on to receive the 1948 Nobel prize in Physiology or Medicine for his work on DDT, despite not actually being a physician or medical researcher. Between 1945 and 1965, DDT's use around the world likely saved tens of millions of lives.

Alarm Bells
More than 1.35 billion lb (612 million kg) of DDT were used between 1942 and 1972 in the United States. Carson's book is given much of the credit for the ban on DDT, but decades before it was published people were sounding the alarm about the possible harm of using so much of the potent chemical. A late 1945 article in *National Geographic* was somewhat hesitant about the insecticide: "Scientists are treading with caution in their use of DDT, because it kills many beneficial insects as well."

By the 1950s, beekeepers and bird fans had filed several lawsuits over DDT's effect on wildlife. And Carson's book isn't the only reason DDT was banned in 1972 in the United States. The Environmental Protection Agency had plenty of scientific evidence that DDT hurt wildlife as well as beneficial insects like bees. It was toxic to marine

US soldiers demonstrating DDT hand-spraying equipment. Yep, that looks perfectly safe...

animals and raptor birds, and was largely blamed for thinning eggshells, which led to almost losing the American bald eagle species completely. After DDT was banned in the United States, the bald eagle population surged, and they were removed from the endangered species list in 2007.

And Now...

Malaria was largely eradicated in the United States decades ago, but when the money ran out for the World Health Organization's malaria eradication project in 1963, there were many countries left in the cold—most of them in Africa. Most of the cases of malaria as of 2017 were concentrated in ten sub-Saharan African countries and India, and the numbers are rising.

But even in countries where malaria has all but disappeared, the effects of DDT live on. You can find research that says DDT is responsible for a whole host of effects on humans, from fertility issues to cancer to autism and more. You can find research that refutes these claims, as well. The truth is, because of its long-lasting nature, DDT is still percolating in our system, both human and natural, and we probably have yet to figure out everything it has done or will continue to do.

Unfortunately, it's also still a very effective way to eradicate the pests that bring malaria, typhus, and other vector diseases, and several countries are still using DDT. Many environmental groups and the World Health Organization today support the use of DDT in some cases to control the spread of malaria—we simply don't have anything else that works as well. As we continue to use DDT as needed throughout the world, the history of its use should demonstrate that it's a balancing act where we have to weigh the number of lives saved against the damage to the environment. Bad yet complicatedly effective invention? Check. Excuse us while we stay inside forever.

#34 THE PLASTIC GROCERY BAG
WHY PLASTIC IS NOT FANTASTIC

1965 | Sweden

Here's an idea: Save the trees and use plastic bags instead of paper bags. Or maybe... don't. Wait. No, definitely don't.

#34 The Plastic Grocery Bag

A brilliantly simple invention that transformed the shopping experience ended up flooding the planet with plastic waste, causing unimaginable devastation to ecosystems. Smart? No, dumb, when the effects are like these.

Around 1 trillion plastic shopping bags are produced every year today—and they're so cheap, strong, and convenient to carry groceries in, they can even contain spills! If only they were easily recyclable and didn't take so long to degrade—if you can call it degrading, that is, since the microplastics they leave behind are forever there. Then the fact that they end up in our oceans wouldn't be such a big deal, huh?

It's a Wrap

The journey of cellophane sacks began back in 1933, when polyethylene was modified for industrial purposes in England by ICI (Imperial Chemical Industries Ltd.). At that time, it was used as an insulator. It's the type of plastic most commonly used in plastic bags, but it wasn't until 1953 that high-density polyethylene (HDPE) was invented, by German chemist Karl Ziegler. HDPE is a stronger, more flexible form of the plastic, perfect for bags. In 1965 the first polyethylene bag was produced and patented in Sweden by Celloplast. It was a Swedish engineer named Sten Gustaf Thulin who designed the plastic shopping bag, and its popularity began to take hold in Europe. He worked at Celloplast on making plastic film "tubing" for industrial packaging and figured out that the tubing could be sealed at the bottom, with handles punched out at the top to create a portable sack. Celloplast patented it and the design hasn't changed much over the years.

Things really took off in the late 1970s when the patent was overturned in the United States by Mobil. Plastic bags were cheaper to make than paper bags, and supermarkets and other retailers gradually switched over to the dark side of single-use plastic sacks. The rest, as they say, is history. Early "carrier" bags (as they are known in Britain) were marketed as better than paper thanks to their soft handles for easier carrying, moisture-proofing properties, and being stronger than paper. Plus, they had multiple uses—it even said so on some bags: for carrying schoolbooks, for beach parties and picnics, as a knitting or sewing bag (hmm, debatable that one, they're not needle-proof, after all...), and as a garbage-can liner.

Hit the Sack

By the end of the 1980s, plastic bags had achieved world domination and replaced paper bags in most places around the globe. It's common to see discarded plastic bags in many areas we go—heck, plastic-bag trash even made its way up to Mount Everest—but the bad esthetics of seeing cellophane sacks caught in trees or blowing across a street are the least of our problems. Many plastic sacks make their way into our oceans (along with other plastic debris), and this is where it gets serious. Masquerading as jellyfish, plastic bags are eaten by sea turtles and cause injuries or death. Turtles aren't the only marine life threatened by plastic sacks: Thousands of sea birds, dolphins, sharks, and whales die annually from either eating or suffocating on bags.

Then there's the microplastics issue—plastic bags eventually waste away after decade upon decade of washing around in the sea and being broken down by the sun, wind, and waves. But they don't fully decompose and instead simply become smaller and smaller, breaking into tiny pieces called microplastics that look a lot like food to your average fish. Sea life ingest them and it's not just their health and survival that is affected: Humans who eat fish and shellfish (whether wild or farmed) ingest the tiny particles of plastics, too. The plastic itself is not the biggest danger to people, it's what it carries that is the problem. Microplastics are perfect for chemical pollutants floating around in the sea to stick to, and stick to them they do. We don't yet know the full effects on the human race of eating plastics, but we do know for sure they're damaging ecosystems.

Not only are they dangerous to wildlife, the cost of cleaning up plastic-bag pollution and processing the landfill they create is enormous. For all these reasons, governments around the world have introduced plastic bag taxes and tried to eliminate plastic grocery bags, around forty years after they were first invented. Bangladesh was the first country to ban thin plastic bags, in 2002, after they blocked storm water drainage during floods that devastated the country. Sten Gustaf Thulin could never have predicted the impact one simple modification to plastic tubing could have caused to the world. And for the rest of us humans, can we all do each other—and the turtles!— a favor and bring reusable bags out shopping? We've got extras if you need some.

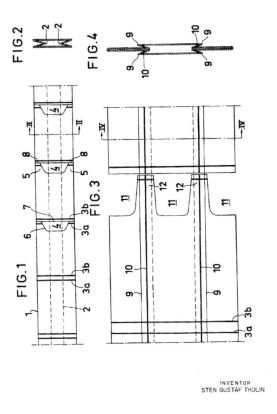

INVENTOR
STEN GUSTAF THULIN

Thulin's ominous patent for "Bag with handle of weldable plastic material."

#35 THE TANNING BED

THE DARKER SIDE OF LIGHT

1970s | Europe and the United States

Sunbeds brought a year-round golden glow within reach of the masses. But what was the real price of bronze?

#35 The Tanning Bed

German scientist Friedrich Wolff devised the first full-length tanning beds and in 1978 started to manufacture them in the United States. Wolff—a researcher investigating the positive effects of ultraviolet (UV) light on athletes who realized that the side effect of exposure, a year-round golden glow, was a marketable proposition—put together UV lamps, mirrored reflector panels, and a safety acrylic shield into a package that would allow tan-seekers to lie down as if at the beach and achieve that sunshine hit even indoors and in the depths of winter.

Exposure to the sun comes with many health benefits—strong bones, improved mood, lower blood pressure, better sleep—but UV rays are highly dangerous and must be absorbed sparingly. Friedrich Wolff's invention was a product initially designed to promote good health and to make people more attractive. Now it turns out his generous gift will actually prematurely age his customers and expose them to a high risk of dangerous and sometimes fatal disease. Whoops.

Fashionable Tans and Heliotherapy

White Westerners' modern preoccupation with acquiring a suntan owes something to French fashion designer Coco Chanel. Her trip to the South of France in 1923 and resultant bronzed exterior set all of the media atwitter way before Twitter and marked a bit of a sea change in the popularity of tans. Before then the fashion was for a paler complexion, and the markets in skin bleachers and tan concealers reflected the mode. For some decades before Coco hit the beach, however, medicine had been discovering the positive qualities of sunlight in combating diseases like rickets and tuberculosis. Faroese physician Niels Ryberg Finsen invented an ultraviolet lamp to mimic the positive effects of the sun portably and in all weathers and seasons to the benefit of sufferers. He received the Nobel prize for his efforts in 1903.

"Heliotherapy" became an accepted benefit. Sick people and kids living in the city were encouraged to go outside and seek the sun's healing rays, to kill off harmful bacteria and to absorb that good Vitamin D. This is produced naturally by the skin on exposure to sunlight and is essential for optimum health. Vitamin D helps produce strong, healthy muscle and bones and is only available in a few foods like oily fish and egg yolks. Sunshine is the easiest way to make sure you have your quotient.

So with these two important boxes ticked—health and fashion—the popularity of tanning gathered apace. The bikini was invented in 1946 so that women could ensure maximum exposure. A tan was de rigueur for that opulent healthy look. Having one said that you could afford the leisure time, the pool, the boat, or even the beach house required for its upkeep. In 1971, even Barbie dolls got a tan. Malibu Barbie came with California beach blonde locks and a deep golden skin tone.

Life's a Beach, and Then You Die

After Wolff developed and marketed tanning beds, tanning salons started popping up all over the Western world, and sunbeds even started appearing in people's homes. A year-round bronze tone became the norm for many people, especially younger women. The golden glow became something you wouldn't leave the house without. An accessory. A necessity.

But dark clouds were gathering. Studies increasingly began to show that UV tanning was a major contributor to skin damage, premature skin aging, and most dangerously, skin cancer. It was discovered that sunburn and frequent exposure to UV rays could greatly increase the risk of developing skin cancer later in life. In 2010, the UK passed a law banning under-18s from using tanning beds. The following year, California followed suit. The scientific evidence had become undeniable, and legislation was stepping in to protect the youth.

Scientists also discovered that even minimal use of tanning beds can increase the risk of melanoma (a.k.a. skin cancer) later in life. One study of sixty-three women diagnosed with melanoma found that sixty-one one of them had used tanning beds in the past. Skin cancer is by far the most common cancer diagnosed in the United States today. With more than 5 million people diagnosed every year, it outnumbers all other cancers combined. But the genie is out of the bottle. More recent studies have shown just how addictive tanning can be. Not having a tan makes young people feel bad. As the tan fades, so do some people's self-confidence, resulting in misery and depression.

Despite the dire health warnings and new laws, tanning bed use is not on the decline. Tanning salons are booming, and sunbed use is expected to continue growing for at least the next five years.

1930s tanning lamp with pipe-smoking model (it's a win-win for cancer).

#36 SUBPRIME MORTGAGES
POP GOES THE HOUSING BUBBLE

2007 | United States

Don't quite understand what happened with the subprime
mortgage crisis and the collapse of the housing market?
The lenders didn't understand how bad it could get, either.

#36 Subprime Mortgages

Banks and other financial institutions are in the business of making money, and when a new opportunity to make money comes along, they don't always ask a lot of questions. Enter subprime mortgages, mortgage-backed securities, and credit default swaps (CDSs). Investors and lenders who didn't have to play by the same rules as banks did some financial sleight-of-hand, lent some money to people they shouldn't have, and lost their shirts when the housing market collapsed.

Building the House of Cards

While Joseph Cassano, an executive at AIG, didn't invent collateralized debt obligations (CDOs) or CDSs, he certainly is the reason they became so popular. AIG would go on to sell about $100 billion of them—which would ultimately lead to their downfall. (Not to worry. The federal government bailed them out.) Basically, the idea behind the CDO and CDS is that if you put mortgages together in a big pool, you can sell shares of it to investors. Between 1998 and 2008, Wall Street was making easy money from these schemes, selling these debt packages to rake in the dough.

And they might have gotten away with it if it hadn't been for those pesky lenders handing out money all willy-nilly. Banks and lenders wanted to get more money into the debt pool so they could make more money—so they started handing out subprime mortgages to people who couldn't really afford them. In a subprime mortgage a bank lends money to people who have risky credit histories or can't prove their income or else the type of loan itself is risky (like an adjustable rate mortgage).

When interest rates fell in 2004, homeowners were encouraged to refinance or to take on risky loans. Many subprime borrowers took on adjustable-rate mortgages, where they got a low interest rate for the first two years—4 percent at the time. After the initial period, the interest rate went up 2 (or more) percent a year, usually getting as high as 10 percent. What did that mean? A $500,000 loan at 4 percent for thirty years was about $2,400 a month. At 10 percent, however, for the remaining twenty-seven years (after the adjustable period ended) the monthly payment jumped to $4,470.

As long as demand for housing remained strong, everything was fine. People could sell their houses before the rate rose, making a profit. However, when housing demand plummeted, there were suddenly a lot of people who couldn't afford their payments.

The House Collapses

Remember that $100 billion in CDSs and CDOs that AIG sold? In 2008, they were suddenly holding a lot of bad loans as people stopped paying their mortgages. Their credit was downgraded, and all those swap investors were able to demand billions in collateral. AIG was at the brink of bankruptcy when taxpayer money bailed them out. That same year, eighty-five-year-old mortgage broker Bear Stearns collapsed, followed months later by Countryside Financial. Lehman Brothers declared bankruptcy that fall. As things start tumbling and the financial collapse picked up speed, the federal government went into crisis mode.

The US Treasury decided to take over management of Freddie Mac and Fannie Mae, which had guaranteed 80 percent of US home mortgages between them. Over the next year, the federal government would also bail out Citigroup, General Motors, Chrysler, and Bank of America—all deemed "too big to fail." The effects of this fallout would cause a Great Recession in the United States, which also rippled throughout other countries. Even today, we're still feeling the effects of the financial crisis.

Lessons Learned?

It's not like the financial institutions didn't have a clue that the collapse was coming. In 2003, billionaire Warren Buffett saw the danger, calling CDSs "financial weapons of mass destruction." And frankly, it sounds like the folks creating the CDOs and CDSs knew that the quality of the loans propping up these pools was getting pretty shaky. Unsustainable growth always leads to the collapse of a market, and it was no different for the subprime mortgage market. Analysis after the fact points out that the problems with these security vehicles would have been spotted a lot sooner if it hadn't been for the housing market boom between 2003 and 2005.

It would be nice to think that everyone has learned their lesson, so we won't have to worry about this happening again. On the other hand, at the turn of the 2020s there was a similar bubble in the student debt market that looked likely to pop, and there are student loan asset-backed securities (SLABS) that function like CDOs. Except, there is no collateral, unlike CDOs—which means investors get nothing in the case of default. In 2019, there was more than $1.5 trillion in outstanding student debt in the United States. Guess it could get worse.

"Financial weapons of mass destruction."

—Billionaire Warren Buffett on CDSs in 2003

Chapter 7

BLAZING
A TRAIL

#37 TREVITHICK'S LOCOMOTIVE

THE LITTLE ENGINE THAT COULD—BUT DIDN'T

1804 | Pennydarren, Wales, UK

Pioneering engineer Richard Trevithick developed a working locomotive that did not work because… it destroyed its own rails. This particular engineer combined the smart and the dumb, the glorious and the disastrous throughout his life.

#37 Trevithick's Locomotive

Known as "the Cornish Giant," Richard Trevithick could throw a sledgehammer over a building at the age of eighteen. One of his schoolmasters described him as "a disobedient, slow, obstinate boy, frequently absent and very inattentive." And there is an undeniably bull-headed quality that surfaces throughout his life, one that led him to hard-won successes and equally spectacular failures. Young Trevithick worked for his father at a copper and tin mine in Cornwall. His size and athleticism would prove an asset in such a physical workplace, but he also showed an early talent for engineering. Specifically, in making improvements to the steam engines used to lift and move ore and refuse from the pits. Richard's passion led him to build his own engines, high-pressure machines that were efficient and powerful.

Under Pressure

Scottish engineer James Watt supplied steam engines for the Cornish mines. They were huge, fuel-hungry, and low-pressure. Watt was wary of high-pressure steam, believing it dangerous. Richard Trevithick was altogether a less cautious character. Starting small, Trevithick made several working models before progressing to full-scale high-pressure engines. These were small enough to be transported by a cart, yet powerful enough to shift heavy ore as well as Watt's leviathans. The dream was to produce a locomotive. To marry the boiler with the engine and put it on wheels. And he did. On Christmas Eve 1801, Trevithick drove his friends up a hill in Camborne, Cornwall, on the world's first joyride. And in 1803, he built another machine that he drove through the streets of London. It was the world's first self-propelled passenger-carrying vehicle. This was all good fun, but the time had come for Trevithick to show that his locomotive was more than a fairground ride. He needed to prove that it offered a practical solution to practical problems. It was time to step it up.

The opportunity came with the Pennydarren Tramroad: 9.5 miles (15 km) of rail that served a network of locations within one of the largest ironworks in the world. Ironworks owner Samuel Homfray struck a bet of 1,000 guineas with a rival owner that he could haul 10 tons of iron from his works to the end of the line at Abercynon. Richard Trevithick was called on to deliver. On February 21, 1804, a huge crowd gathered to witness the attempt. Five trams were loaded with iron and seventy men clambered aboard to make up the weight. When the chimney of Trevithick's engine struck a low bridge early in the journey, it destroyed both. But Trevithick was able to fix the chimney and complete the journey, and Homfray collected on his bet. Unfortunately, due to the gradient, the engine was unable to complete the return journey. Equally unfortunate, the engine was so heavy that rails were broken and had to be rebuilt. This happened again, and again, and after three trips, the locomotive was retired. You'd think they'd have asked him to stop.

In 1808, Trevithick built a circular track to take passengers round and round in Torrington Square in London. An actual fairground ride! But the rails broke there, too, and the engine fell over. Whomp, whomp. Trevithick's cycles of glory and failure continued for the rest of his life. He went to Peru to build engines for silver mines, but the War of Independence broke out and his machines were destroyed by revolutionaries. He went to Costa Rica, trying to mine gold, but he ran out of funds. Eventually, a young Robert Stephenson, later dubbed "The Father of Railways," paid Trevithick's passage home to England. Richard Trevithick, whose ideas and machines had advanced the cause of transport as much as anyone, died penniless and disappointed at the Bull Inn in Kent, in 1833. He was a failure. Albeit a glorious one.

> ## "A disobedient, slow, obstinate boy, frequently absent and very inattentive."

—Schoolmaster's assessment of Richard Trevithick

On paper, Trevithick's engine looked good...

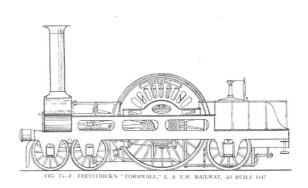

FIG. 75—F. TREVITHICK'S "CORNWALL," L. & N.W. RAILWAY, AS BUILT 1847

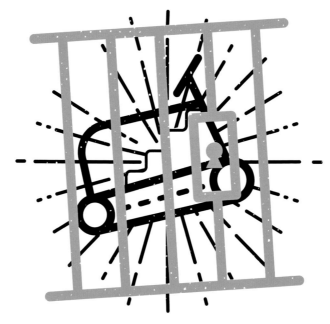

#38 THE TREADWHEEL
EVERLASTING STAIRCASE OF PUNISHMENT

1818 | Norfolk, UK

The stepping machine is widely recognized as torture by gym-goers. But not many people know that it really was invented as a punishment device, for nineteenth-century prisoners. The point was for it to be pointless, but then it became pointless…

Engineer William Cubitt came from a family of millers, so when he was asked to design a punishing regime for convicted felons, the answer was obvious to him: the treadwheel. It wasn't a new idea as such, since similar devices already existed on a smaller scale.

Cubitt's machine was a bit like a large water wheel for milling flour. It was a long cylinder that was 6 feet (1.8 m) in diameter, with steps all around the wheel. The idea was that prisoners would climb an infinite staircase, giving them a tough workout and plenty of time to think about what they'd done. The first penal treadwheel was installed in Bury St. Edmunds jail in Norfolk, England, and could hold around thirty prisoners at a time. The torture instrument was initially a success and was snapped up by many other prisons in England.

Daily Grind

The root of the idea for the treadwheel was to create a penal device that put criminals to good, industrial use, perhaps grinding flour while they toiled—hence the term treadmill was used interchangeably with treadwheel. The early nineteenth-century prison system was pretty brutal, though, with many convicts sentenced to "hard labor," so weights were added to increase the resistance of the machine and there was no purpose to turning the wheel other than to pass time in the punishment of stepping and stepping upward but never getting anywhere.

It was a miserable psychological punishment as much as a physical one. And woe betide any prisoners who decided the infinite climbing was not for them: "Arms and bludgeons" were used on slackers, to persuade them to keep going. Later, the treadmill served more of a purpose, as originally intended, and prisoners did grind grain and pump prison water with their efforts.

And they were no small efforts—for six hours each day a prisoner would step on the ancient StairMaster precursor, with a five-minute break every fifteen minutes. The

A punishing treadwheel above prisoners playing freeze dance in the yard.

work was carried out virtually in isolation as each prisoner was blocked off from the others on the wheel by means of wooden-screened cubicles. When combined with solitary confinement, the chronically tiring treadwheel seemed pretty successful in creating submissive, exhausted prisoners.

Stepping over the Atlantic

By 1822, news of the punishing treadwheel invention had traveled across the pond to the United States, and a handful of American prisons installed the treadwheels. Inmates ground corn while climbing the endless wheel, to feed fellow prisoners as well as local almshouse residents. Penitentiaries even had viewing platforms installed, where citizens could watch and heckle the forever-stepping prisoners.

The American prison ethos at the time was to teach convicts a trade that was useful to society both during their time in jail as well as afterward. The treadmill was a helpful addition to prisons for those inmates who couldn't quite master technical crafts such as shoemaking or metal forging, and for those who were doing a short stint inside and didn't have time to learn a craft.

The efficacy of this form of punishment was backed up by a physician's report, which deemed it "peculiarly irksome; requiring a severe exertion of the body, but furnishing no employment of the mind." However, it was this "irksome" quality of the treadwheel that caused its eventual demise—in prisons, at least, since today we are happy to pay for the privilege of using stepping machines in pursuit of a workout. The fact that the results of the hard toil weren't easily evident began to demonstrate that using prisoners as an energy source probably wasn't the best way to rehabilitate them long-term. The treadwheel took otherwise productive felons away from making useful goods such as furniture, mailbags, and clothes, so it seemed a no-brainer that the treadwheel was soon abandoned in American prisons.

In England, the reward-less punishment was adopted for much longer and endured for the rest of the century, until advances in technology meant machines became a lot more efficient than manually powered mills, so their usefulness except as punishment became redundant. British prison reforms in 1898 outlawed this type of inane, brutal discipline in favor of rehabilitation and treadwheels were finally abolished in the early 1900s. Except in your local fitness club, that is. Enjoy.

Crank It Up

Not content with the treadwheel as punishment in prisons, another hard-labor torture instrument was devised, called the crank. This was an arm-powered wheel bedded in gravel or sand to create resistance (more gravel was added by hard taskmasters, to make it even harder to turn). Later designs had screw-adjusted brakes that jailers could turn up or down depending on how much they wanted to punish the convict, who had to turn the handle thousands of times a day.

#39 EDISON'S ELECTRIC PEN
TELEGRAPH-STYLE PRINTING

1876 | Newark, New Jersey

The celebrated inventor's fast-printing device—inspired by the electric telegraph—might have been a success but for the development of typewriters that could do it better...

#39 Edison's Electric Pen

Thomas Edison had high hopes for his electric pen copier set, which he launched in 1876. The inventor was working on telegraphy research one day, looking for further improvements to be made to the original telegraphing system devised by fellow-American Samuel Morse, which employed Morse code. Edison's system used letters, rather than dots and dashes, punched out of the strip of paper feeding out from the machine at the "receiving" end of the telegrams being sent.

Edison noticed a different use for the device. The rapidly hammering stylus leaving tiny holes in the paper strip might be producing a stencil—a piece of paper with holes in it that you could roll ink over to make lots of copies. So on March 13, 1876, the prolific inventor rushed to the patent office and filed patent No. 180,857 as "autographic printing," and devised the electric pen set to be sold in shops.

The Gift That Keeps on Giving

The set came with an ink roller and flatbed made of cast iron to place your paper on, a pen holder, and a "pen." The pen was actually like a little jackhammer, wired up to a battery to make it—according to the instructions—bounce up and down fifty times a second, producing small holes in the paper you were writing or drawing on. Once your stencil was finished, you could then place it on the flatbed on top of a blank sheet of paper and roll ink over it, making perfect copies time after time.

Edison claimed that no fewer than 5,000 copies could be made from a single stencil. More than enough to sell out a theater with flyers handed out in the street, for example—or start a revolution in a smallish country with a tactically distributed incendiary political pamphlet.

Edison declared his electric pen a success, and trumpeted sales of 60,000, but in truth his accounts reveal sales of fewer than 4,000 sets, while the highest serial number found on any existing examples is 8739.

What Went Wrong?

Well, first the battery was essentially a jar of dangerous chemicals in need of fairly constant maintenance, preferably by someone qualified to handle them without killing the dog or burning a hole in the carpet. Second, the mini-jackhammer comparison didn't stop at the design and construction of the electric pen. It also accurately describes the noise it made when you used it. It's hard to write revolutionary pamphlets when any neighbors within a 600-yard (548-m) radius of your basement can hear you fomenting discord at 3 a.m.

Third, the invention of typewriters that could be adapted to make stencils, in around 1884, would make the electric pen obsolete. In fact, Edison was working on one of those himself. This didn't go down well with Chicago customer George Bliss of the Western Electric Company who, having placed a standing order for 200 pen sets a month, was alarmed to read in his newspaper that Edison was about to render his stock worthless. "I can scarcely believe this to be possible and shall be glad to have you advise me what the facts are!" he fumed. But Edison had moved on. New products to make, new markets to conquer. The inventor wasn't happy unless he had filed at least three new patents before breakfast. George Bliss was probably still trying to shift electric pens at yard sales twenty years on. Poor George.

"Like Kissing—Every Succeeding Impression is as Good as the First"

—Advertisement for Edison Electric Pen

Electric pen design (doubles as a mini jackhammer).

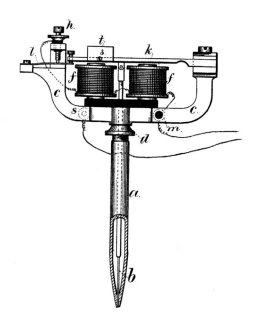

One Man's Trash Is Another's Treasure

For every George Bliss there is a Samuel F. O'Reilly. Samuel was a New York City tattoo artist born to Irish immigrant parents in 1854. O'Reilly simply replaced Edison's pen tip with a needle to push ink into skin. The rapidly moving needle made tattooing much quicker and transformed the industry overnight. Tattoos became quicker, less painful, more affordable, and, suddenly, super popular. A report in the *New York World* estimated in 1897 that three-quarters of the society women of the United States were now inked. After registering patent No. 464,801—the electric rotary tattoo machine—in 1891, former burglar and ex-con Sam became the world's first electric tattooist, inker to the famous, the most celebrated practitioner of the art anywhere in the world. So, while the usefulness of a jar of lethal chemicals attached to a mini jackhammer was not a money spinner for George Bliss or even for Thomas Edison, one Irish innovator found a pot of gold at the end of that particular rainbow after all.

#40 THE HELIO MOTOR
HERE COMES THE SUN

1900 | Arizona

Harnessing the sun's rays to produce enough heat to melt iron and generate a new, cleaner form of electricity seemed like a great idea in 1900, but some people thought it was dumb, which meant it never took off—at least, not yet...

#40 The Helio Motor

It was the sun beating down on him in Arizona that gave Dr. William Calver the idea for a new kind of power. Calver, who had experience in engineering and in running mines in the Southwest United States, knew how scarce fuel was in the desert state, but the sun was in plentiful supply. He founded Calver Universal Power Company and set about building a machine that could bottle the sun's rays in Arizona. And, by all accounts, it worked. However, using the sun as an energy source wouldn't really take off until decades later... Smart ideas often need good timing, and if they're ahead of their time, people ignore them or misunderstand them and see them as dumb.

There was history behind the idea. Ancient Greek scientist Archimedes used mirrors to direct the sun at ancient Roman ships and set them on fire, according to author Lucian in the second century. This "heat ray" has been recreated in modern times to varying degrees of success, and similar devices have been built in recent years called heliostats or solar furnaces. But when Calver was working on his many solar patents, incinerating ships with sunrays felt like myth, and there had been only sporadic attempts in the nineteenth century to put the sun's energy to use. Calver's Helio Motor was a series of frames of 1,600 mirrors that could focus the rays of the sun onto a concentrated spot, creating enough heat to boil water and melt iron.

Calver wasn't humble about his achievement. "I have solved the problem of the direct conversion of the sun's rays into a heat which can be utilized on a far cheaper commercial basis than coal," he said. "I have also devised a method for the storage of this heat so that it can be used at any desired time and place." His storage system made use of stone, earth, and other non-conductors to store the heat. He told reporters at a demonstration in 1900 that the small reservoir he had with him had stored heat and kept the temperature high enough to boil water a week later. Investors lined up to throw money as his invention, and Leland Stanford (yes, the one that Stanford University is named after) stated, "The steam engine made a great revolution and this will make another."

Blazing a Trail

News articles at the time were also a bit breathless about the Helio Motor, running down the ways in which Calver's invention would change industry and modern life forever. "It is almost safe to prophesy that in the future, instead of coal-bins and wood-sheds, every house will have its sun-motor, for the cost is practically nothing," stated an article in *Pearson's Magazine* about the Helio Motor in 1900. Journalists saw it changing the way the world worked in the same way the steam engine had—from industrial manufacturing to cooking dinner at home for pennies. One author pointed out that the mirrors of the invention baked bricks twenty times as rapidly as a kiln and so hard "as to scratch case-hardened steel."

Ahead of His Time?
Unfortunately, Calver's idea didn't take off at the time. His energy storage system was just too inefficient, and the Helio Motor could be difficult to use. Also, inertia is hard to overcome, and why would industries spend money to change their ways when coal worked just as well and was already in use? The Helio Motor also likely lost momentum when its inventor died just eight years later.

The good news is that he was merely ahead of his time. Concentrated solar power (CSP) systems, very similar to his Helio Motor, are now using mirrors or lenses to concentrate sunlight onto a small area. In 2017, CSP systems made up less than 2 percent of the world's solar electricity plants, but prices are falling and the need to start using more clean energy is very real. Also, CSP systems have an advantage over the solar panels that are showing up on more and more rooftops—they can store energy in such a way that they can produce electricity day or night. Finally, more than a hundred years after he first demonstrated his invention, the spark of Dr. Calver's idea is starting to catch fire.

Dr. Calver showcasing his Helio Motor invention.

#41 THE ONE-WHEELED MOTORCYCLE

ARE YOU SITTING COMFORTABLY?

1904 | United States and Europe

Who needs two wheels when one will do?
Even on a motorcycle? Enter the monocycle:
It was like a unicycle... only death-ier.

#41 The One-Wheeled Motorcycle

The first monowheels were invented in the 1860s and motorcycles arrived in around 1885. The first motorized monowheel? In 1904, the Italian House of Garavaglia unveiled one at the Milan Exposition. Considered the first motor-powered monowheel, it had a large chair—think dining-room chair size—that was positioned in the middle of the tire and had a gasoline engine. Wow.

Transportation had been evolving since the wheel was invented: People wanting faster ways of getting from here to there... Then wanting weirder ways to accomplish the same thing. When bicycles, or velocipedes (the earliest bikes), were invented, they gained popularity quickly. As ownership grew, the number of these transportation devices seen in cities across the world might be compared to ants raiding a picnic. Authorities in some cities wanted them banned because they were pests. People were racing around, trying to see how fast they could go. Some rapscallions even biked down sets of stairs.

Travel Like a Gerbil

The first monowheels moved away from a rider on top of a unicycle or bicycle and instead had a large tire that the rider sat inside. The tire rotated around the person! These strangest of strange vehicles were either cranked by hand with a wheel on waist-high gears or pedaled with feet—like bikes. When stopping abruptly or moving too fast, the driver would make a full rotation with the wheel. This resembled a gerbil on a wheel, that loses control when the speed is too high and hilariously spins around and around until it flies off, landing stunned, wondering what the heck just happened.

No one person can be credited with inventing the monowheel. Three patents were all filed within a short period of time in 1869 in the United States for hand-cranked ones. Others were filed for foot-powered ones in the same year in Europe. Newer models and ideas kept popping up. On a typical two-wheeler, the wheels work together. One moves it forward and the other helps it turn. When it's only one wheel doing all the work, it is doing both. Easy to move forward, not so easy to steer. Most monowheels used the rider's body position to change directions, meaning a slower pace was needed.

Can of Worms

Who wants to go slow? Sloths? Using feet to change directions, leaning the body, tiny wheels set in a track, steering wheels, and sometimes gyroscopes were all methods used to maneuver the monocycles. Without the last two, they fell over easily. The 1904 Milan monowheel had a training wheel sticking out of one side for balance.

Over the next thirty years or so, design after design of motorized monowheels would be introduced. Some were quite simple looking. Others were flat out bonkers. The cover of the April 1914 *Popular Mechanics* featured one designed by Alfred E. D'Harlingue of Missouri that had a 5-foot (1.5-m) propeller attached to the front. Cheating? Another, looking like something right out of a sci-fi movie, was referred to as the "New Terror of the Road" by *Everyday Science* in 1923. Designed by E. J. Christie from Iowa, it was a 14-foot (4.3-m) wheeled monster, propelled by two 500 lb (225 kg) gyroscopes, an airplane motor, and weighed 2,400 lb (nearly 1,100 kg). Christie hoped it would go as fast as 400 mph (650 kmph)!

In 1923, the version that's now associated with a basic powered monocycle was Italian designer Davide Cislaghi's Motoruota—Italian for "motorwheel." He patented the design in France in 1924 and the UK in 1927. His had rollers in a track that helped the outer wheel stay on course, a steering wheel, and a single-cylinder engine. The innards were able to tilt to the sides to handle cumbersome corners, so some visuals show the rider hanging off to the side. This should have helped with the overall drive experience but balancing on them was tenuous and riders often ended up struggling as they tried to remain upright or they toppled off to the side. Plus, there was a built-in obstruction while operating it. You know, the tire that was continuously turning in front of the driver? And because speed demons obviously wanted to go fast, it was completely unsafe. In the end, monocycles just weren't practical. Only a few were ever sold by any company. Two-wheeled bicycles and motorcycles won the battle of the bikes.

Monocycles are now produced by and for hard-core hobbyists, seen in sci-fi movies, and used in kitsch places like the "Robot Restaurant" in Japan. Here's hoping that one day, monocycles will be seen flying down the highway, driver in mid-gerbil.

Monocyclist selfishly not giving his dog a ride.

#42 TEFLON
THE STICKING POINT

1938 | Jackson, New Jersey

Good thing, bad thing. A chemist accidentally discovers
the substance behind nonstick pans. But making it releases
atmosphere-damaging PFCs and using it can release toxic gas.

Refrigeration has been a definite plus for humanity, and not just for the luxury of enjoying a chilled beverage on a warm day. Food kept at low temperatures keeps fresher for longer. In the quest for refrigeration, chemists were playing with all sorts of chemicals and coming up with some interesting (if rather dangerous) substances, which is where Teflon—discovered by Dr. Roy Plunkett of DuPont in 1938—came in.

Ice Ice Baby

Thousands of years ago the Egyptians and Persians used evaporation to cool their larders, hanging wet cloths from a ceiling and reducing the temperature of the room in which food was being stored. Around 1000 BCE the Chinese were filling pits and cellars with ice in winter time, to enjoy the cooling properties well into the warmer months, and these two methods, evaporation and collecting ice, were pretty much how we cooled stuff right up to the early and mid-1800s, when ice was bought and sold and transported around the world for cool boxes in people's homes.

The use of more advanced chemistry in cooling started earlier, in the mid-1700s, with people like American polymath Benjamin Franklin and John Hadley—a professor of chemistry at the University of Cambridge in England—experimenting with evaporating alcohol and ether to achieve satisfyingly low temperatures, enough to make ice form on a thermometer.

Kind of Cool

In the 1800s, the chemists had moved on to altogether more dangerous chemicals. English scientist Michael Faraday managed to liquefy ammonia gas using pressure and cold and by the middle of the century the first machines for air-conditioning and the first refrigeration units were being produced. The problem with using volatile and extremely toxic refrigerants was that they were, well, volatile and extremely toxic. Enter Dr. Roy Plunkett. He was employed by the DuPont chemical company to try to find a less dangerous and less toxic substitute refrigerant, one less likely to explode and/or leak and poison everyone in the immediate vicinity.

I Don't Know What It Is, But I Like It

One day, Plunkett was experimenting with a likely contender when he discovered that his liquid appeared to have polymerized. It had turned into a white, hard, waxy substance. Not what he was looking for. On further investigation, however, he discovered that this substance had some extraordinary qualities. First, it was inert virtually to every other chemical. Nothing seemed to have an effect on it. Second, it was incredibly slippery. And third, it appeared to be able to withstand ridiculously high temperatures before melting.

Roy had accidentally invented Teflon. And that turned out to be both a good and a bad thing. The inertness meant it could be used for containers and pipework that carried other chemicals, even dangerous ones. Teflon turned out to be the perfect material for storing the uranium hexafluoride used for the first atomic bomb, for example. Teflon's high melting point and incredible slipperiness meant that it was useful in space exploration, for protecting vehicles under high temperatures during re-entry into the Earth's atmosphere and even for the clothing that astronauts wore. Neil Armstrong was wearing Teflon-coated boots when he walked on the Moon.

Teflon quickly became one of the most versatile substances ever. The applications were seemingly endless, from commercial and industrial uses to domestic products like stain-resistant clothing and carpets, food wrap, pizza boxes, and microwave bags. Its most famous application is for cookware. Being capable of withstanding super-high temperatures and being literally the most slippery substance ever discovered turned out to be pretty much the perfect requirements for what would become the world's first nonstick pan. A pan that you didn't have to clean burned omelet from after use. It was the holy grail for lazy and inattentive cooks all over the world.

But there is a major caveat. Teflon can withstand very high temperatures, it's true. Nothing happens to it up to about 600°F (315°C). Unfortunately, if you leave a pan on the stove for five minutes, 700°F (371°C) is easily reachable. And at those temperatures, Teflon starts to release a toxic gas. "Polymer fume fever" symptoms include coughing, headaches, and fever. But bad as it is for humans, it is quickly terminal for any pet birds in the home. And, it turns out, the manufacture of nonstick compounds releases polyfluorocarbons (PFCs) into the atmosphere. These count as "greenhouse gases," which make the atmosphere retain heat more effectively and contribute to global warming. So in his search for a less toxic substance to use in fridges, Roy Plunkett accidentally found a more toxic substance to use on just about anything.

Courtesy of the Hagley Museum & Library

Dr. Plunkett with his invention.

INDEX

CREDITS

Page 42

smell-o-vision, Gmhofmann [CC BY-SA 3.0 (https://creativecommons.org/licenses/by-sa/3.0)]

Page 150

DDT, USDA—This image was released by the Agricultural Research Service, the research agency of the United States Department of Agriculture

Page 155

plastic bag, Google Patents

Page 189

Hagley Museum & Library, Wilmington, DE 19807